From
Galaxies
to Man

Other books by John Pfeiffer

SCIENCE IN YOUR LIFE

THE HUMAN BRAIN

THE CHANGING UNIVERSE

From Galaxies to Man

A Story of
the Beginnings of Things

By John Pfeiffer

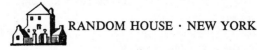 RANDOM HOUSE · NEW YORK

FIRST PRINTING

© COPYRIGHT, 1959, BY JOHN PFEIFFER

ALL RIGHTS RESERVED UNDER INTERNATIONAL AND PAN-AMERICAN
COPYRIGHT CONVENTIONS. PUBLISHED IN NEW YORK BY RANDOM HOUSE,
INC., AND SIMULTANEOUSLY IN TORONTO, CANADA, BY RANDOM HOUSE
OF CANADA, LIMITED.

LIBRARY OF CONGRESS CATALOG CARD NUMBER: 59–12308

DRAWINGS BY SOL EHRLICH

MANUFACTURED IN THE UNITED STATES OF AMERICA
BY THE KINGSPORT PRESS, INC.

Acknowledgments

IN *On the Origin of Species,* published November 24, 1859, Darwin did not discuss human origins and prehistory. But the implications were quite clear. His contemporaries were most impressed with a notion considered revolutionary in Victorian times—the notion that man has evolved, is evolving and will continue to evolve.

A century of research since then has demonstrated the essential validity of Darwin's investigations and insights. Even more significant, it has indicated that evolution is a much broader concept than was originally realized. As far back as we can trace, matter has been organizing itself into more and more elaborate patterns, and life represents a part of the same inclusive process. Over the ages relatively simple forms tend to give rise to series of varied and intricate forms in a kind of chain reaction of increasing complexity.

The word "evolution" is often used to describe the shaping and extinction of stars and planets as well as living species. We read about species of molecules and the evolution in primeval seas of new chemical systems, the gradual emergence of animate from inanimate matter. To a greater extent than ever before, physicists, astronomers, geologists, chemists and biologists are finding common interests in the development of the solar system, and the origin and spread of life.

This book has developed out of discussions over a number of years with many scientists in various branches of research. Preliminary interviews and library studies took place at the Marine Biological Laboratory in Woods Hole, Massachusetts. I owe a great deal to the director of the Laboratory, Philip Armstrong, and to its trustees. Because of their co-operation I had the opportunity of meeting investigators and talking with them at leisure in ideal surroundings.

During the final organizing stages I spent several weeks at the California Institute of Technology, and the following list includes some of the investigators who gave generously of their time: Walter Baade, George Beadle, Harrison Brown, Robert Christy, Max Delbrück, William Fowler, Murray Gell-Mann, Jesse Greenstein, Norman Horowitz, Paul Merrill, Matthew Meselson, Rudolph Minkowski, Guido Munch, Claire Patterson, Linus Pauling, Allan Sandage, Robert Sinsheimer, and A. H. Sturtevant.

Among those who helped me at other institutions were Elso Barghoorn and Ernst Mayr of Harvard University; H. J. Muller of Indiana University; Theodosius Dobzhansky of Columbia University; Daniel Mazia of the University of California; Seymour Benzer of Purdue University; S. Chandrasekhar, Gerard Kuiper, W. W. Morgan and Carl Sagan of the Yerkes Observatory of the University of Chicago; Loren Eiseley of the University of Pennsylvania; Patrick Hurley and Victor Weisskopf of the Massachusetts Institute of Technology; and John Bonner and Martin Schwarzschild of Princeton University.

For many reasons it is important that books about science present information against an international background. As a matter of general policy, they should be based on visits to foreign as well as American laboratories. This is not always practicable, chiefly because financial support has not been widely available for those attempting to bring science to nonscientists. I am therefore most grateful to the Department of State for a Fulbright grant which made it possible for me to spend four months at the Naples Zoological Station, a leading biological research center which provides research and library facilities for investigators from many nations.

A major part of this book was written at the Station, largely because of the warm hospitality of its director, Peter Dohrn— and the expert advice and guidance of his co-workers, G. Ghiretti and Pierre Tardent. I am also indebted to Guiseppe Montalenti and Eduardo Scarano of the University of Naples, for technical assistance, and to Salvatore Bottino of the United States

Acknowledgments

Information Service in Naples, who opened many doors for me and played a large part in making my visit enjoyable as well as productive.

Special mention should be made of the time and effort spent in my behalf by Helen Brownson, William Consolazio and John Wilson of the National Science Foundation. Their active interest and support did a great deal to encourage me when it seemed that I would not be able to complete the book. They furnished me with introductions which paved the way for discussions with the following investigators abroad:

Francis Crick, Fred Hoyle, Leslie Orgel, M. F. Perutz and Martin Ryle of Cambridge University; Kenneth Oakley of the British Museum (Natural History); John Bernal of Birkbeck College, London; Rudolf Altevogt, Angela Nolte and Bernhard Rensch of the University of Münster; Heinz Holter and Martin Ottesen of the Carlsberg Laboratories in Copenhagen; Hendrik van de Hulst, Jan Oort and Martin Schmidt of the Leiden Observatory; Jean Brachet of the University of Brussels; C. Jeuniaux and Claude Libecq of the University of Liege; and Johannes Hürzeler of the Museum of Natural History in Basel.

These and other investigators contributed to the book by furnishing information about their research and discussing speculative ideas freely. Some of them did service far beyond the call of duty by checking individual chapters. They have done all they could to help make this a useful presentation.

The photographs used in the illustrations were kindly provided by investigators at the Mount Wilson and Palomar Observatories, the Franklin Institute, the High Altitude Observatory in Climax, Colorado, the Basel Museum of Natural History, the Biological Laboratories of Harvard University, the General Electric Research Laboratories, and the Upjohn Company.

Contents

Illustrations

DESIGNED BY Sol Ehrlich

From
Galaxies
to Man

The Beginnings
of Things

1

A JAPANESE legend tells of a wanderer climbing a mountain road at night. Somewhere ahead he hears a woman sobbing. He climbs further and sees her standing by the side of the road, her back to him, her face buried in her hands. He walks over to where she stands and speaks to her. But the woman does not turn. He speaks again, this time putting his hand on her shoulder. And this time she turns and lets her hands fall to her sides. Her face is blank as an egg, featureless—without nose, mouth, lips, eyes.

A long time ago the face of the universe was blank. Once where the Milky Way is now there was only an immensity darker and stiller than an underground vault. Matter was atomized, spread out into a mist so thin that an observer would have seen nothing. Matter diluted to an almost-perfect vacuum. With every breath, each of us inhales more atoms than could have been found at that time in ten billion cubic miles of space, a volume thirty times greater than that of all the world's oceans. A faint scent of substance in the void. No lights to punctuate the blackness, no glowing landmarks, no horizons, no constellations. Nothing to see or steer by, nowhere to go, no travelers. A loneliness far more terrible than death. There was nothing to die.

A stark, improbable setting for beginnings and births. Only dispersed and unshaped substance in the blackness, and time—perhaps ten billion years or so. A past so remote would have meaning for a race of beings as large and long-lived as the stars, beings who roamed the universe the way we roam one of the sun's satellites. A race of gods, if you will. They could comprehend what to us must appear as forever. Our capacity to comprehend or to care is limited to lesser pasts.

Ten billion years ago. A long, long flight back over the deserts of times past, beyond the memory of oases and mirages. In that flight the entire span of human history and prehistory is the upstroke of a single wing beat. A few moments ago, on that time scale, hunted creatures no longer apes and not yet men wandered in packs in a world which still belonged to stronger and swifter animals. Their brains were not much larger than the brain of a newborn infant. They were wiped out, and so were the men who first brought fire into caves and talked and had notions about life and life after death. Forefathers without Mayflowers, pioneers without covered wagons, they endured for a while in wildernesses wider and wilder than any we know. Yet few of us are concerned about them and their pedigrees.

Even millennia are too much for us. Even Egypt and Stonehenge seem ancient, ancient and remote. We may think back to times when we were younger, and think ahead to old age and to a time when we shall no longer exist—a few decades either way. A greater span is somewhat academic as far as feeling deeply is concerned. Our

4

pride and nostalgia and fear and all the things we love involve a pinpoint in time, are bounded by a century.

Ten billion years ago something took root in space and started growing. The blackness was a beginning, not an ending. A cloud formed, a cloud bearing little resemblance to those in today's skies. Our clouds are dense, granite-solid, by comparison—heavy with ice crystals and dust and water droplets and grains of burned-out meteors. That cloud was still thinner than a sigh, but not as thin as what had been before. There were stirrings in the cloud. Slowly matter drifted together in a kind of inanimate herd instinct. Matter stirred and thickened, and the blackness was shattered. The lights came on, fireflies in immensity. The lights were stars, showers and clusters of stars, and incandescent knots of clotting gas which were nesting places for new stars.

In some places matter thickened still more, and became the hard crystal rock stuff and the oceans of planets. And on one of the planets at least, the waters and the crystal mixed. Out of the mixture came living things embodying a new sort of restlessness, a built-in restlessness that had acquired a momentum of its own. Once life got its foothold, it dug in and persisted and evolved and spread like fire whipped up by the wind in a forest of pines. Feeding on lifeless mineral stuff. Sopping up the light of the sun. A warm blue flame spreading over the crust of at least one planet, consuming the crust and multiplying. The cloud in the terrible blackness at the beginning was not a place of death. No catacomb, but an enormous seed.

The cloud was made up of a universal raw material. The cloud has gone but its original substance still exists. Its atoms—packed together, condensed, arranged and rearranged—are now the billions of stars in the Milky Way, the sun and the planets, the concrete and steel that go into our superhighways and cities. The ink on this page, the paper, the machines that print books, you who are reading—all

5

these things are made up of the same atomic particles which once existed in another state in the original cloud. Everything, everywhere, is the primordial and enduring cloud stuff transformed.

A process is under way, a process which arose in chaos. For the original cloud was chaos, "that old confusion wherein without order, without fashion, confusedly lay the discordant seeds of things." From cloud to us, a process which feeds on chaos and generates patterns in a special way. We walk on the seashore and see ripples in the sand, ridges and furrows whose symmetries mark the places where wind and water have passed. Sea-swell rises in rolling humps offshore and, rising higher, begins to break and shows a curving underside before it turns to surf and spray.

Such shapings are essentially repetitions, variations on old themes. Once nature learned the making of such patterns, she did it over and over again. There were similar patterns, patterns no more and no less intricate, in the sands and waters of primeval seashores, in a gray rock-world bare of trees and grasses and flowers. There will be similar patterns on future shores, in future seas, in the debris of granite cliffs that are not yet sand. Many patterns, snow crystals and gullies in eroded rock and mountain cones and craters, have this same repeating, unevolving quality. The processes which formed them work today as they have always worked.

The basic fact about the process which started in the cloud is that it gives rise continually to novelty, to things differing radically from what existed before. It generates not only patterns, but patterns of increasing complexity. Or, to put it another way, matter has been organizing itself into increasingly complex patterns. The cloud has evolved and the universe will never again be the same as it once was. Raw substance, once scattered sparsely through vast stretches of space, has shaped itself into a succession of more

6

and more elaborate forms. Of all known forms we are the latest and most elaborate.

The sweep, the unfolding, of a process. From cloud to us. If it had all been recorded as a motion picture, a spectacular to end all spectaculars, we could sit back and watch the reel run backwards. A brief sequence dealing with the present: my room, a speck in a particle of space called Pennsylvania, a tiny, compact center of highly organized substance. The room overlooks a garden and a yard near a canal and contains a desk and chair, shelves of books, radiator, typewriter, radio.

First flashback. The same spot a hundred years ago. Now the house has vanished and there is a stretch of uncleared land by the side of the canal and a barge on the canal, pulled by mules, is bringing coal to the sea. Dissolve to second flashback. The same spot again, further back in time, say three or four centuries. Canal and barge gone. A hollow place in a dark forest, a floor of leaves, and the trace of a trail pressed in leaves. Close-up: a hunter passing through as silent as the prey he stalks.

Flashback Number Three. Forty millennia before that, still the same spot, a winter scene. Man and his prey have fled nearer the equator, and the old forest is buried deep under snowdrifts. It is the time of the last major advance of the glaciers. Not far off, a moving ice cliff more than a mile high, a bulldozer from the north crunching rocks beneath it.

The reel unwinds faster. Ages whir by, and we see what it looked like here three or four hundred million years ago. No life on land. Whitecaps on a shallow inland sea. Smoke and rumbling on the horizon to the right, from the chimney vent of a black island volcano. More unwinding and faster still. Scene: gray rock everywhere, a desert, part of the elephant-skin crust that first covered the earth. And now things dissolve. The desert fades, the rocks evaporate to seething gases. We stand like Mephistopheles amid flame. Until the final sequence: the light goes and we are in the blackness that came before hells, in the original chaos, the original cloud.

Evolution in reverse, spiraling back to an almost-nothingness, a blank beginning. Comparing things then and things now, we see more clearly what has passed and what grows. A series of cosmic events has reduced the blackness and the facelessness. The chaos has become less, and patterns animate and inanimate have increased. The main theme of everything that has happened is growth and blossoming, beginning after beginning.

We know all this because the past has left traces. It moves like a restless live thing, padding along strange new trails in twilight places. Sometimes the past goes boldly through fields and deserts and wide-open spaces, roaring its presence, making marks defiant for all to see. For example, the regal and ringing proclamation of the Pyramids. Sometimes the past shouts at us.

Sometimes the past cries out across distances in remote and lonely places. Sometimes the past protests the passing of beauty, the neglect of beauty that has not passed, the belittling and patronizing that robs death of its dignity. Clun Castle ruined and alone as a lost child on a little hill in Shropshire. A family graveyard on a mountainside in Vermont, and the Brahman cows grazing just outside the iron fence. Broken pillars seen across a wasteland, silhouetted against a sunset in Palmyra. Sometimes, as if it also were lost and alone, the past cries out to us.

And sometimes, more often than not, the past hides from us. The past moves underground and we, its pursuers, go digging after it. Sometimes underground there is a hint of rustling, a shadow passes or we think a shadow passes, or a hunch—why not look here? So we turn and do something, and all of a sudden we may stumble upon the hiding past and meet it face to face with a thrill of surprise. Digging a little way through soil and gravel near the surface, deeper among ashes and the post holes of burned huts, and the skeleton of a fallen defender. Driven like a wedge between two vertebrae, the iron head of an arrow shot nineteen centuries ago from a Roman bow.

Surprises. An archeologist sits on an ancient wall, eating lunch after a morning of uneventful work. Another wasted day? His legs dangle, he looks at his shoes and past his shoes to an excavating pick lying on the floor. Not far off he sees a broken-through place in the floor, patched with cement. The patched-up spot happens to be near the pick, so he lifts the tool and drives its point into the cement. Casually, idly, just to be doing something. "What happened then is graven on my memory." The cement comes away, and the dark soil beneath the floor is suddenly covered with a strange green confetti. A shower of old bronze coins, a treasure hoard from the Dark Ages.

Traces, marks whose deliberate patterns imply meaning and purpose. Symbols preceding the coming of alphabets describe recipes, cures, profits and losses, births and deaths. A cracked tablet from Babylon. Cuneiform signs, impressed with a wedge-shaped tool on hardened clay, tell of drowned men and drowned cities and the gods in anger—the legend of an ancient deluge. A discus found in Crete, covered with picture writing in a spiral pattern, undeciphered. Stylized flowers, branches with leaves, birds and men running and sharp-snouted fish. They tell us nothing. The past is mute at times.

And the past may tell in color of fears and feelings and visions older than writing and as old as man, almost. Robot, a fox terrier with black ears, vanishes at the edge of an oak forest on a hill in southern France. Vanishes from the surface of the earth. Four boys searching for Robot look everywhere and miss nothing. The youngest boy kneels near a

9

shrub: "Here. Over here!" A little hole in the ground half-covered with moss, half-choked with the exposed roots of the shrub. Could Robot have gone that way, down that fox-hole?

It is no foxhole. The boys clear dirt away, and stones and roots. The hole becomes larger, large enough to crawl into. The oldest boy scrambles in, flashlight in hand. His feet disappear. "It's getting wider. . . ." Then the sound of sliding earth and stones, and the oldest boy's voice echoing and reverberating from a hollow place underground: "Robot! Robot!" The other boys push themselves into the hole, slide down, join their friend in the cave. A whistle, and Robot hears and his leaps are heard from a distance. The dog is found. But the adventure has only started. The youngest boy, the boy who owns Robot and who found the hole near the shrub, sees something else.

A horse, ready to leap, painted beautifully in reddish-brown oil paints on a wall of the cave. And other horses, all galloping. A whole picture gallery. A herd of stags with great antlers, a large black bull with angry eyes showing white, a rhinoceros and many other animals. Only animals, except in a kind of sunken spot or crypt where the ground dips steeply down into the darkness.

There, in the most secret, least accessible place, the boys find a picture including man and death. A man falling backwards, as if fainting or in a trance, and near him a huge bull-like creature, horns lowered and ready to attack—and dying, belly ripped open by a spear driven through its body. The boys whisper and wonder what it means, for the paintings in the cave tell of rituals and old magic and totems and the changing and growing of beliefs. We still have much to learn about the boys' findings, and about similar paintings by other artists who worked in the remotenesses of other caves two hundred centuries or more ago.

Dig into deeper, darker places where prehistory has been

and burrowed its blind way and left more marks underground. A trail so faint that only skilled hunters of the past can follow it, and so subtle that even they may be misled from time to time. A trail of things shaped by hands that were not quite human hands: split pebbles, crudely chipped flakes, choppers. Mixed among the tools, the enduring bones of the half-men who worked the raw stone—and before the making of tools, there are only bones in the record.

A dynamite blast in South Africa, in a limestone quarry north of the Kimberley diamond mines. An observer, standing a bit too close, has a narrow escape. Out of the corner of his eye he sees something black falling through the air, and jumps back and throws up his hand to protect his face. A chunk of rock thuds at his feet. He picks it up and stares at a death's-head. Imbedded in the rock and only partly broken, something hurled from the past. A small, gray, eroding skull. The skull of a child, more than a million years old. Relic of an extinct breed, not a man but not an ape either.

Our part of the past a flicker in time. And before us, the ages. Practically everything that has happened, happened before we came. The false record: Fossils found and disbelieved and misinterpreted. Assorted bones fitted together to confirm a myth, to form the skeleton of a unicorn. The skull of an ice-age rhinoceros "reconstructed" into a long-necked flying dragon with dagger teeth, and a statue of the dragon stands in a German town today. And the true record, just as strange: Eggs and footprints fossilized. The imprint of a flying reptile, wings broken and collapsed where it fell. Fossil fish, each bone etched clear for the record; trilobites with many little legs; spiral shells; coral fronds. Fantastic patterns. Trails of the moving past frozen in stone, the past caught in its tracks like a night prowler in the beam of a searchlight. Back a hundred million years, two hundred million years, half a billion years—and much further.

Iron for ships and rockets and bridges and cloverleaf intersections. Industry feeding on iron and feeling the pinch. Current deposits becoming exhausted, and the search for new sources. A geologist conducting a survey for U. S. Steel tramps where there are no roads, through a Canadian wilderness of rock and wind-beaten bush, along the northern shores of Lake Superior. He stops and sinks his pick into black shale and black dehydrated opal. He collects samples and carries them in a knapsack on his back and brings them with him to his laboratory.

Then, the dissection of mineral. Rock sliced with a diamond-edged saw into sections a thousandth of an inch thick, pages of a crystalline album. Sections placed under the microscope indicate the possibility of new ores that may be mined when present supplies dwindle. The company will be very interested, and this goes into the geologist's notebook. The microscope also shows something else, something unlooked for and of less immediate concern to the company: "I nearly fell off my chair, it was so exciting."

The past is whispering now, distant and in an alien language which experts in crystal and the ways of crystal may help interpret. Once, long ago, continental masses of granite shattered and hot waters rose from underground springs and flowed over the fragments, boulders bigger than houses. Lime and silica were dissolved in the waters and, with the passing of time, precipitated to form layers of mineral over parts of the boulders. A thin crust on solid stone. The crust was a tomb of a sort, for it covered and trapped something alive—a green slime, like the slimes on the surfaces of stagnant ponds.

Under the microscope, a section of the crust and remains of the ancient slime look like jackstraws in a matrix of jelly. Petrified protoplasm. The fossils of blue-green algae, primitive cells which bred and spread in thin sheets over the pitted surfaces of dead gray rock. Animated films of the living past. This part of the record goes back a long way. The slime flourished nearly two billion years ago, and even then life was not new. Single cells are complex things. There must have been simpler forms before the slime, but if they left fossils we have not yet found them.

For times more remote, before alphabets and artifacts and fossils, there are different kinds of evidence. Scantier evidence leaning more heavily on inference. Deductions and calculations and theories. Experiments that may last for years and yield one set of accurate numbers. Facts fitted together and checked and rechecked and crosschecked, until we round off the jagged edges of individual inspiration and arrive at plausible sequences. Data replacing myth. Or, if you will, the coming of a new variety of myth which can be confirmed and rests on collective insights.

Spelling out the course of recent events is challenge enough. What happened on the night of April 4, 1950? Even in the absence of deceit, the fallibility of memory is sufficient to warrant trials and juries and judges and lawyers and stenographers and court clerks. But seeking clues to the greatest of all mysteries, reconstructing the activities of the remote past, which involves times without nights or calendars or formal records of any sort, is a somewhat subtler task. For this we need experiments, data, imagination.

Clues, in the workings of radioactive clocks. The silver-white metal uranium is a natural metronome, a time-keeping device of high precision. Its unstable atoms explode rhythmically, in pulses of millions per second, at a rate which earthquakes and glaciers and molten lava cannot alter. Spontaneous transmutation. Uranium atoms decaying to lead, uranium-lead ratios indicating the ages of the most ancient things. Wherever the metals exist we may compute dates. We deduce our beginnings from the oldest exposed rocks, from minerals dug out of the deepest mines—and from pieces of shooting stars formed together with the earth and planets when the solar system was young.

Sometime during the Dark Ages or before, a white-hot boulder, scarred and pitted and jagged, came roaring out of the skies and crashed on the desert of Arizona. The Canyon Diablo meteorite crashed and burst like a bomb, the detonation forming a crater more than fifty stories deep and nearly a mile across. A millennium or so later an investigator in California grinds fragments of the meteorite to sand, dissolves the sand and analyzes it chemically. It contains traces of lead, one part in three million, end-products of decaying uranium which existed before there was an earth. Other analyses of other meteorites and of terrestrial rocks, computations and columns of figures, and the evidence checks roughly, give or take a few eons. The past is dated again and again, and we have another beginning: the formation of the earth and the solar system, about four and a half billion years ago.

The hunters of the past explore deeper and deeper in time. Toward receding sources. Along highways, side roads, lanes, alleys, footpaths barely detectable whose mileposts are yesterdays. A long, long, chain of yesterdays like a string of lights on a vast suspension bridge stretching across black waters, trailing off into wide horizons. Back to the first yesterday, to the beginning if there was or is a beginning. Back toward the coming of the galaxies and the original cloud before the lights went on.

These beginnings lie in outer space, among cities of stars. Astronomy, a population study of remote settlements in inaccessible regions, where events are under way which tell us indirectly about local events, happenings in the neighborhood of the sun. Parts of the story of our own past and possible futures. Telescopes designed to scan the skies for evidence which the naked eye cannot detect, to gather light from the stars. The light is passed to other instruments and analyzed. Star after star over the years, and the records pile up. The census taking proceeds, accumulating vital statistics

14

—ages, longevities, physical conditions, compositions, birth rates and death rates. Astronomers deduce the shape of events which occurred six, eight, ten billion years ago. The cloud and the origin of the cloud and the beginnings of our universe. Beyond that, clues are much, much harder to come by and even the imagination feels its limits.

The past is everywhere. In the rainbow spectra of dissected starlight, in rocks formed on earth or in the space between planets, in petrified wood and bone and in the prints of wood and bone that have rotted away, in flaked flints and pictures painted underground, in tombs and temple monoliths and monuments buried and not yet buried, in manuscripts kept under glass, in file cases crammed with old correspondence and legal papers, in yesterday's newspaper, in the storehouses of the human brain. The past is everywhere, pervading and persistent as memory, moving behind us like a shadow.

Records from many sources, of many kinds, and interpretations more often wrong than right. In the seventeenth century an English bishop dated a beginning: the earth was created at nine in the morning, October 26, 4004 B.C. Before him Hindu writers cited the earth's age as exactly 1,972,949,-048 years. The illusion of accuracy. Precision where there was none and still is none. Dogmas and fiats and pontifications. As if nature could be known by edict or approved by testimonials.

But always learning, almost despite ourselves, and the record becomes clearer. It tells of the basic process from original cloud to life and us, matter evolving patterns of greater and greater complexity. The process has not ended. We are not a final achievement, a pattern arrived at and completed. We are a new beginning in the restless flow of things, the latest but not the last in a series of beginnings which bring novelty into the universe—and thereby continually replenish surprise.

15

The process, stage one: the origin of matter. We can speak of many beginnings, but was there a first beginning? Was there once absolute emptiness, an infinite vacuum? And if so, how did substance come into being and when? To such ultimate questions there are no answers. But given matter, given a cloud of primordial and relatively simple stuff in a highly disorganized state, one thing follows: the physical universe as we know it today, born out of chaos and generating pattern. Given a cloud of thinly dispersed atoms, the clottings and condensations proceed according to their own laws, the rules of an unfinished game played in the immense arena of space.

Inanimate matter in all its forms. A succession of symmetries. The swirl of gases in spiral galaxies. Globes of gas burning as stars, red and yellow and blue and white. A brood of planets moving about the sun, bound in orbits, held by invisible cords. One planet, the earth, a ball of stone with a molten core, and caps of ice and oceans clinging to parts of the crust like films of moisture. The crust, and beneath the crust, rocks hardened into patterned fragments, crystals needle-sharp and clean-faced and many faceted. The most perfect examples of inanimate symmetry. High points in the early evolution of matter.

The process, stage two: the origin of life. In unagitated pools, in basins beyond the reach of violent tides and the surf, in places where nothing much seemed to be happening—a revolution takes shape. Strange brews simmering in sunlight produce something different from crystal. This stuff does not endure by rigidity. It is soft, yielding. And not as beautiful as crystal, in the beginning. An animated scum, a moving jelly, born in water. It resists changes by changing ceaselessly. The secret of the whirlpool whose substance drains always away and whose form persists.

Living things, whirlpools that reproduce. Blobs of protoplasm that breed and do not always breed true—and be-

16

cause they do not always breed true, all things are possible. Small changes at first. Offspring resembling parents for a time during early generations. But there is a universe of time. Thousands and hundreds of thousands of generations pass. Small changes build up and accumulate until it may be impossible to comprehend how what is developed from what was in times long past. Like rumor. A tale altered somewhat with each telling, and barely recognizable after many tellings. Images and near-images and a burst of new patterns. Tentacles and electrical organs and eyes that grow on stalks, shells and wings and claws and brains. A flood of species, novelty spilling over the earth.

The process, stage three: the origin of man. We are stage three, matter built into something new and unprecedented, a radical innovation. We are stage three at its very beginning, the first trials in an experiment which has scarcely started. Our voluminous records of ourselves deal with an infinitesimal span in the scheme of things. Imagine gathering from all the world's libraries all existing records of man. His prehistory and history, his fairy tales and poems and religions, his crafts and industries and games. Books, monographs, encyclopedias, texts, journals, newspapers, everything collected in one place. A metropolis of libraries, mountains of publications higher than Himalayas, covering a past of negligible dimensions on a cosmic scale. All these records involve a period equivalent to one second, one tick-tock of a clock, in a twenty-four-hour day.

We are all future. Another universe lies ahead, a long sequence of ages that have not yet been used for evolving, a new wilderness of time and space to be explored and cleared and scarred with the ruts of long use. For such futures prophecy is rarely attempted. Who could have predicted what has come from the original cloud, from raw matter almost completely unorganized? Who could have predicted the spirals of Andromeda, the rings of Saturn, the earth with

17

meteors and thunder in its skies, living slime? Given the first forms of life, microscopic or submicroscopic things in vast waters, who could have predicted whales and peacocks and eagles and tigers and men?

Today, given man, the future is similarly obscure. We only know that we are a beginning as revolutionary and significant as the original cloud or the earliest living things. And as far as we know, we alone can ask questions, can wonder what we may become.

Our story is of the beginnings of things. It concerns the remotest of all events, events which took place ages ago. Parts of the past are utterly inaccessible. They are the ultimate gaps in our records. We shall never be able to prove once and for all how the stars were formed. Even if celestial engineers somehow managed to manufacture a star in some vacant lot along the Milky Way, it would be no proof that nature had used the same methods.

So we must speculate, although it need not be blindly. There is evidence of many kinds. Night watchers dwarfed by the high domes of observatories turn telescopes to places where new stars are being born today, take photographs and compare records, and consider tentative explanations for what the records show. From such investigations we can deduce certain things about how stars now in their prime or aging may have been formed in times past. Other work bears on beginnings less remote, but still sufficiently far away to elude final explanations. Studies of basic problems are yielding insights far more penetrating than could have been expected a decade or two ago. There is new research on the origin of the solar system and the earth, and on the origin of life and species and man. We are ruling out notions that contradict or fail to account for the facts, and indicating possibilities.

The beginnings of things. There are endings also, endings everywhere, senilities and deaths among stars and satellites

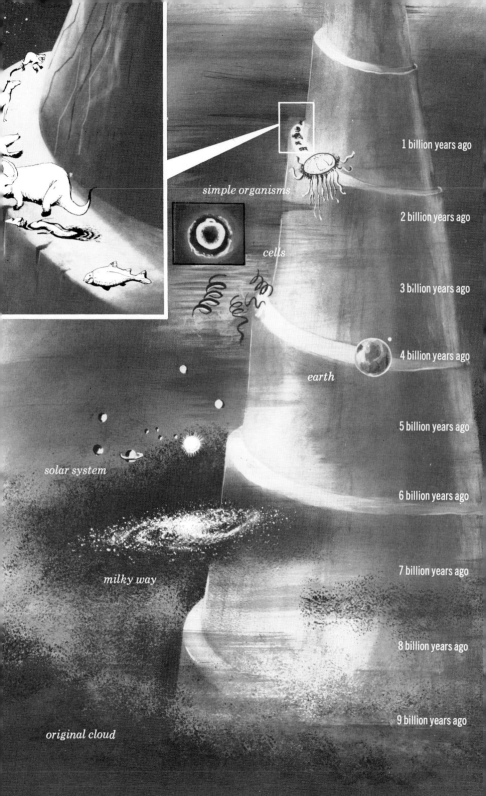

simple organisms

cells

earth

solar system

milky way

original cloud

THE ORGANIZATION OF MATTER

1 billion years ago

2 billion years ago

3 billion years ago

4 billion years ago

5 billion years ago

6 billion years ago

7 billion years ago

8 billion years ago

9 billion years ago

10 billion years ago

ROCKET FLIGHT INTO MILKY WAY SUBURBS

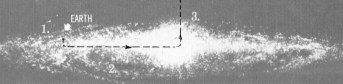

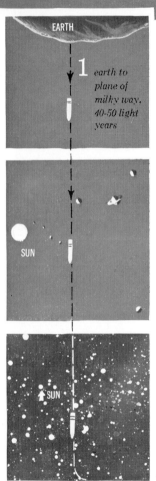

1 *earth to plane of milky way, 40-50 light years*

EARTH

SUN

SUN

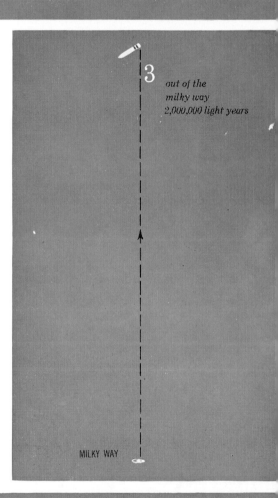

3 *out of the milky way 2,000,000 light years*

MILKY WAY

2 *to center of milky way, 30,000 light years*

as well as among living things. There are endings everywhere, and at times we focus on them, view nature in terms of our private endings. But to do this is to miss the point. The dominant process in the universe has been a creative process that generates novelty in the midst of seasons and cycles and all repeating, unevolving things. New and unexpected and increasingly complex patterns form in the midst of patterns that have existed for eons. In such a framework death is a by-product, a theme incidental to the main theme, essentially an accident. Our emphasis is on beginnings and births.

MATTER

A Universe

of Galaxies

2

FIRST, the shape of the cosmos in perspective, a bird's-eye view of how matter is organized in the universe as we know it today. Our theories about the beginnings of things must take account of patterns which have already evolved, so we start with an exploration of space—an imaginary trip in a rocket capable of going anywhere at any speed we choose. A glorious free-flying rocket that shatters time, complete with food and living space and portholes.

We leave with a roar and catch a quick glimpse of a whole curved section of the earth. Already at the very first stages all signs of human activity have vanished, all our homes and roads and cities. Already the earth is strange and unfamiliar. There are great stretches of ocean and shining bays and mountain ranges and white cloud puffs far below. All this for an instant only. As the earth moves away like a projectile in retreat, we see it rounder and shrinking.

Little by little things drop further and further away. The panorama broadens to include, one by one, the other planets. Until we look back and down and see for the first time the solar system as a whole, the sun huge in the center. And an entire family of spinning illuminated globes. Four little spheres nearest the sun: Mercury, Venus, Earth, Mars. And then four large spheres including Jupiter, the largest of all, voluminous enough to hold more than a thousand earths with room to spare. Finally, spinning near the outskirts, another tiny globe, Pluto.

Beyond that we might see a glowing region, a haze of dust and crystals and fragments of stone, possibly the debris of a tenth planet which exploded when the solar system was young. This may be a breeding place for comets. Sudden disturbances may thrust material toward the sun on a new orbit, and a new comet streaks among the planets. We see all this, like a model moved by an invisible and noiseless motor, satellites and satellites of satellites. Orbits within orbits, motions so regular that we can understand how earlier investigators were misled, and believed in the mechanical necessity of things and a universe running like a great clock.

We pick up speed, for our trip has just begun. The planets disappear, with Jupiter the last to go. At a distance of more than a billion miles we still have a landmark. The sun is still large. But it is shrinking the way the earth shrank at the start of our trip. More time passes and the sun is just visible as one among many, many stars, a faint and unsteady light which deserves one farewell look. That beacon is our last contact with the region in space where the earth is. It is like leaving one's homeland for a long trip, and watching a friend waving good-by until the gap between boat and pier becomes so wide that we see him no more.

Now the sun has disappeared. We have traveled about fifty light-years, a light-year being more than six thousand billion miles, and we veer sharply for a ninety-degree

24

change in course. We have been traveling in a region of villages in outlying districts, on second-class roads. Now we are on an enormous turnpike in the skies, toward the center of the Milky Way. The sun is a small home in the country, and we are headed for more densely populated places where the lights are brighter. It is some twenty-seven thousand light-years to the heart of the metropolis.

This superhighway is no more exciting than most of the superhighways on earth. We move swiftly, but nothing is intimate. We pass stars, legions of stars, but at such great distances that it is impossible to make out details. In fact, the odds against close approaches are high. The stars may be hundreds of thousands of miles in diameter and weigh billions and billions of tons, but they are extremely small compared with the distances between them. Like fireflies over a forest, and each firefly separated from its nearest neighbor by twenty miles.

But we are lucky. At one point we happen to come relatively close to a star, at least close enough to see its family of satellites—alien planets illuminated sharp and clear, as if in a stage setting, so that they show crescent and half-moon and full-moon phases. And we are reminded of our sun and our earth, and wish we could stop. The landscape passes like a home with lights seen from a train at night. We are back again amid immensities and remote stars, after our brief encounter with another sun.

Another strange event occurs near the beginning of our trip toward the center. We notice fewer and fewer stars, until we can see less than a hundred lights where there were thousands before. Later there is an abundance of stars again, and still later another diminishing. This time all but half a dozen of the stars fade away. Things become pitch-black, darker than the deepest crevices of a cave, and for a while we fly blind through space. We are passing through clouds of gas and dust, clouds of all sizes, miles or light-years across.

We notice that changes in the number of visible stars are greater and more frequent during certain parts of our journey, in certain stretches of space where many clouds are concentrated. Between these stretches we move for long periods through relatively clear places, where clouds are sparser and our view is rarely obstructed.

We notice something else, something we have been expecting. Allowing for the effects of obscuring clouds, there are more and more lights as our trip progresses. The skies are becoming more and more crowded with stars and patterns of stars, rich material for the outlining of new constellations. And we remember other skies, skies which are now thousands of light-years away near our sun, and they seem dim and threadbare by comparison. We know we are approaching a main terminal in our trip, coming closer and closer to the center of the Milky Way.

Now we have arrived. We stop at the very center and our rocket hovers, a shining metal tube suspended inside a globe of lights. The lights are everywhere, all around us, and the long night here is not at all like the nights we knew on earth. On those nights we could see only a few thousand stars, but on this night the skies are on fire and there are many hundreds of thousands. Here it is always bright, bright as the full moon, bright as the nights on earth in northern regions where you can read without lamps at midnight.

We hover for a while to watch the display. Then the trip continues, with a special purpose. On the first lap of our journey we left the solar system, rising high above its plane and looking down on it from above and seeing it as a whole with its patterns of orbits. Now we want to achieve the same thing for the entire Milky Way, to view in all its immensity the structure in which the solar system is like a mote of dust in a cathedral. So we make another ninety-degree turn, tilting the nose of our rocket "up" toward an outer surface of

26

the central globe of stars, for these skies are not infinite and there is an edge.

Our rocket climbs between and among the stars, and on beyond the stars. Out of the central globe, just beyond its edge. Before this stage of the journey we have always traveled in interstellar space. We have always had stars around us, in all directions. Now we are leaving the stars behind, and we look down on a bulging surface, part of a dome, the central globe of stars seen from the outside. We continue to soar and look down as the Milky Way shrinks and retreats, until it gradually begins to appear in full perspective.

At last, thousands of light-years above the center, we see the Milky Way as a whole. Except for that bulge in the center it is a flat thing, a mammoth disc floating in a void. A flying saucer of a sort. We are so far away that only the brightest, hottest stars are visible, as brilliant blue and white lights. But they are excellent markers. Strung out like chains of Japanese lanterns that fade off into the distance, they illuminate the spiral arms of the Milky Way. Twisted tentacles of gas are wound up around the center, whorls resembling traces of giant fingerprints. The spiral shows us that the disc is spinning like a record on a turntable. Most of the obscuring clouds we encountered on our way to the center were in the spiral arms.

And still we climb, and the platter grows smaller. We see none of the Milky Way's stars, only the bright center and the glowing spiral arms. We speed on and stop once more, the last stop of our outward flight, more than a million light-years from the Milky Way. It is a blur now, just barely visible. If we had not traveled through it and above it and observed its structure, we might mistake the blur for a small cloud of gas not far off. But we know the blur for what it is— a flattened, spinning swarm of stars which includes the sun and the planet which was our take-off point. An island in an

27

ocean whose shores have never been found. A galaxy, our galaxy which we have named the Milky Way.

Suspended in a wide and starless night, we look about us casually and see nothing. Or almost nothing. Was that a glow over there? We look again, this time more carefully, and locate another blur far off in the darkness. And further to the right, even fainter, the suggestion of still another blur. That is all we can see from here. Two more blurs, two more Milky Ways. We must be sure to keep our bearings, now that there is a risk of traveling toward the wrong blur. The prospect of becoming lost is a chilling one. We might enter an unfamiliar galaxy, involve ourselves in a labyrinth of stars, and never get home.

But we make no mistakes on the return trip. We go back the way we came. First, a long, whining nose-dive a million light-years down into the core of the Milky Way, where the stars are thickest. Then leveling off out toward the rim, along the central plane of the disc. At a point about two-thirds of the way from center to rim, we leave the main highway and take the side road to the solar system, to our village in the skies. Finally, the home stretch. Navigating toward the earth, a pinpoint target circling around the sun. Our aim is good. We approach the target, swoop down, decelerate, and come to rest among men. Home.

The adventure is over. We have steered our rocket into interstellar space. We have passed stars by the millions, seen another solar system, entered the heart of the Milky Way. A long, long journey by terrestrial standards. But nothing special in terms of remote regions whose light takes more than a million millennia to reach us. Hardly more than a Sunday excursion, a ride to the end of the line and back on the local bus.

Yet even this trip is enough to indicate a few important facts about the way things are organized in the known universe. For example, we do not find stars scattered everywhere throughout the depths of space. They do not sail alone in the skies like liners and merchant vessels and yachts in the seas. Stars come in great fleets, grouped in formations called galaxies. Some galaxies spin with spiral arms like our Milky Way. Others are bright globes or are egg-shaped; still others appear as curved filament-like structures which resemble the letter "S." There are also the irregulars, which have no particular form.

Every galaxy is a distinct aggregation or swarm of billions of stars. The stars remain together and move together as a unit. In all directions, beyond the boundaries of our home galaxy, there are other galaxies floating like luminescent moths, clouds of stars drifting through space as far out as we can see. At least half a billion such galaxies lie within the range of our largest telescopes, and we have not reached the limits, if any, of the universe.

Half a billion galaxies, at a conservative guess. Galaxy after galaxy, patterns of many kinds that keep changing. An incessant shaping of matter. Spinning systems sucking in filaments of gas, parasites feeding on the diffuse stuff between the stars. Everywhere an apparent richness of substance being formed or forming. The mass of our moon, the lone satellite of one planet revolving around one star in one galaxy—about sixty billion billion tons. The mass of half a billion galaxies? It would be an impressive-sounding total mounting to a digit with fifty or so zeros strung out after it.

But the void is so much vaster. Matter is extremely scarce in comparison with the unimaginable abundance of space. The galaxies are tiny spots, specks of glittering diamond, few and far between and lost in the stretches of a near-perfect vacuum. If all the galaxies were redistributed, if all the substance of all the galaxies were spread evenly throughout space, every 1,000,000,000,000,000 cubic miles would contain only about an ounce of matter. The universe is a sparse place, almost as insubstantial as a ghost. The difference between things as they are and utter, stark emptiness is the merest trace of substance barely contaminating the void. A trace representing the difference between existence and nonexistence.

Out of this almost-nothingness, everything. And we wonder about the beginnings of the long process that has produced us and will yet produce much, much more. We wonder about the nature of things before galaxies came, scan space for answers or the possibility of answers, and find an expanding universe. In all directions, wherever we look, the galaxies are moving further and further from one another. The gaps between them are widening all the time, and the most remote galaxies are receding from us at the highest rates. Certain galaxies, for example, have increased their distance from the earth by nearly 200,000 miles while you were reading this sentence.

Things seem to be flying apart, as if a shell had burst in midair and the galaxies were shrapnel. In fact, the explosion or "big bang" theory about cosmic origins is based on a similar notion. According to this theory, all the matter of the universe was once concentrated and jammed together into a superdense mass of atoms—a compact aerial mine many times larger than the sun, a bomb waiting to be detonated. Then, about ten billion years ago, the charge was somehow set off and exploded in a flash of radiation. The substance hurled outward by the explosion is still speeding off into space in the form of gases and radiation and galaxies in an expanding universe.

Here is melodrama enough for a dozen theories, a story of fireworks on a grand scale, and sudden cataclysmic creation. Another theory is less spectacular to describe, but far more revolutionary from a philosophical point of view. It revives in modified form the medieval heresy of Bruno, who was burned at the stake for expressing such beliefs—the concept of an infinite universe, a boundless universe with no beginning and no end, no Creation and no Doomsday.

Today some astronomers, Bruno's twentieth-century successors, regard the expanding universe in similar terms. It has been expanding through all eternity, and will continue expanding forever. Although galaxies have been receding from the neighborhood of the Milky Way for countless billions of years, the total number of observable galaxies has not changed. Many galaxies have long since passed into regions beyond the ranges of our telescopes, and many more are currently in the process of doing so. But the observable universe never "empties."

As fast as old galaxies recede and fade and vanish from our field of vision, they are replaced by an equal number of fresh galaxies. The newcomers are formed from new matter, which is continuously created at just the rate necessary to maintain about the same population density of galaxies in space. The rate is exceedingly slow, too slow to detect by present-day methods. In a volume of space about as large as a modern skyscraper, one ton of matter comes into being every ten million years or so. At that rate, for the universe as a whole, enough matter is created every second to make fifty thousand suns.

In other words, acccording to this theory, the universe is a self-regulating system in a state of delicate balance. Unlimited in extent, it is so adjusted that as it expands, the average over-all density of any large portion of space does not change appreciably. This is the steady-state universe. It resembles an infinite pool which loses substance steadily, and is steadily fed and refilled by fresh material. Incidentally, the general notion of the continuous creation of matter is not a new one either. Bruno conceived it more than three hundred years ago: "There are no ends, boundaries, limits or walls which can defraud or deprive us of the in-

31

finite multitude of things . . . For from infinity is born an ever fresh abundance of matter."

These theories and others, of necessity, beg the basic question of how matter originated. In the explosion theory, the universe had a beginning when every particle of matter was to be found within a great concentrated mass. In the steady-state theory, the universe is infinite in time, has no beginning, and matter arises continually. But whether matter was created all at once or is created little by little at an unchanging rate, the mystery of its source still remains. Conceivably matter could be formed on a large scale from pure energy, in a process the reverse of that taking place in nuclear weapons and furnaces which obtain energy from annihilating matter. But when we ask where the energy came from we find ourselves chasing a physical will-o'-the-wisp, the fleeting shadow of a question. At present the ultimate origin of matter is a problem outside the realm of fruitful speculation. We must take matter for granted and proceed from there.

Unshaped substance in an expanding universe, raw material for many galaxies and among them a Milky Way with stars and planets and life. For the forming of galaxies no process has been worked out in precise detail, but we have a plausible idea of the general drift of things.

Ten billion years ago. A dilute cloud, dispersed more finely than the finest mist, moves like a puff of smoke through a wasteland of space. A cloud of hydrogen gas millions and millions of light-years across, and nowhere a meaningful feature. Nowhere a signpost. An unlit, cold and lonely cloud without structure, without pattern. Matter distributed evenly, one region of space indistinguishable from the next. Everything the same, everywhere.

The cloud is a placeless thing—like a Levittown with unending streets and every house exactly like every other house and no numbers on the houses and all the people in all the houses with identical faces. The cloud is wide and cold. In *Moby Dick*, Pip the cabin boy falls out of the whaleboat and the whale hunters will not stop. They pass on, leaving him there alone on a floating spar in the sea. A day and a night later the whale hunters come back to pick him up, and Pip has gone mad from the loneliness. The cloud is a wider and colder and more awful sea.

A cloud, dilute and monotonous and featureless. A desert adrift in a void, barren of pattern. This is a transient kind of chaos in the scheme of things. Such blankness, an almost utter lack of structure, cannot endure indefinitely. There seems to be a stubborn pattern-forming tendency in matter.

We mourn the passing of patterns, man-made and -begotten. Imperial roads that are now rubble. The crumbling of temples and towers and the walls of homes. The burial of whole cities in sand and lava. The succession of dyings which no spring and no blossom can console. But it is the patterns which multiply and spread and evolve. The record shows that it is chaos which passes.

The end of chaos comes quietly, as imperceptible as a passage from night to dawn. We can never know for certain what took place, but it was probably not sudden and not dramatic. The most significant changes often occur in places where nothing much seems to be happening. There are stirrings in the cloud, like the sluggish waters at the ocean surface signifying the beginnings of commotion underneath. Perhaps a gradual drifting together in one region of the cloud. Perhaps parts of the gas happen to merge and form a zone of slightly increased density. Slowly a clump exists, where particles of matter attract one another by their gravitational pull—and the force holds them together in a loose but sufficient bond.

The clump is a primordial nucleus, a strange inanimate cell. A fertilized ovum which will begin changing in a new way and split like a cell and breed galaxies and eventually generate an entire procession of living things. The clump grows at its own pace. It attracts streams of matter and becomes larger—and the larger it becomes, the stronger its pull and the more matter it attracts. As when a group of people collects in the streets, and is joined by more and more people until a huge crowd has gathered. A self-feeding, self-accelerating process yielding a thicker and thicker blob of gas. The cloud pulls itself together, shrinks. Things start stirring on an increasing scale.

Matter is jostled and confined. The cloud becomes a restless sea of gas, heaving and swirling and rushing. Restless with the rolling of invisible swells, the breaking of invisible waves each larger than a continent. The crash of wave against wave, the piling up and crisscrossing and overlapping of waves. Prodigious surf in the skies. And all the time everywhere, briefly in the midst of commotion, patterns appearing. Faint shapes in a fermenting cloud, like shadows on a screen.

Here the hint of a spiral, a swirl of circling stuff and an eddy starts to spin. Then another flurry and the swirl is swept away. It is a death, in a sense; a defeat. A tenuous possibility vanishes, incipient pattern dispersed in a puff, and disorder continues to dominate—for a time. Other patterns come and go. An arch of gas curves high, poises, and collapses in a shower of spray. A streak passes like a rocket in the night and spends itself and sputters out. Patterns, but not enduring patterns. Premonitions of enduring patterns. Things that might have evolved if they had not faded so swiftly. This happens many, many times and ages pass and still nothing endures.

All this is surmise, based on the study of models, model clouds similar in certain ways to the cloud that spawned the Milky Way. But the clouds are not actually produced in the laboratory for carefully controlled studies. It would be wonderful if we could build an experimental void, a perfect vacuum in a space at least as large as Grand Central Terminal, and add to it a dash of hydrogen gas and watch the gas contract and develop into miniature cameo-like galaxies. Perhaps some day, but not in the foreseeable future.

Instead we construct different kinds of models, models pieced together in the mind with the speed and precision and freedom of thought. We can conceive of a void of any size and use our current knowledge to introduce into it a specific temperature and density—all in our heads—and then learn what would happen by solving the appropriate mathematical equations. Mathematics involves the building of imagined models, the running to completion of processes which we cannot observe directly.

So we use mathematics to watch in imagination the workings of one model, to study the cloud. It shrinks to about one-half its size in three billion years or so, and then stops shrinking. What will happen next? Our equations describe one possibility. The cloud is seething so violently inside that it heaves and pulsates like an embryo growing, and it starts to expand again and continues expanding until it almost attains its original dimensions. It is still seething inside. There are mighty tides, winding and meandering currents moving at hypersonic rates. Jets in the cloud, but not narrow like those which form the wake of a plane or a missile. Some of the jets are high-velocity Gulf Streams, rivers so wide that a spaceship traveling at the speed of light would take many thousands of years to fly from one side to the other.

The cloud is unstable under such conditions. Sooner or later its substance must redistribute itself, and the currents may have a great deal to do with what happens. Some of the jets may break away from the cloud, or two jets may sideswipe one another or meet head on, splashing a great mass of gas into space. In any case, the cloud bursts into fragments. Not like a shell, not all at once, but by stages in a kind of chain reaction. The first bursting produces four or five fragments perhaps, and then each fragment divides into further fragments. The process continues until there is a swarm of small clouds where one super-giant existed before. Of course, these new clouds are small only by comparison with the original. Each of them is large enough to hold billions of solar systems.

Time passes, and now we pay special attention and watch one of the subclouds, a particularly massive body which measures from 300,000 to 500,000 light-years across and is still without shape. We watch something mounting to a crescendo of movement—figuratively speaking, a louder and louder rolling of drums. The subcloud spins and contracts, and the more it contracts the faster it spins, like a siren or a musical top that whines to a higher and higher pitch. Faster and faster, and the sides bulge out as if an urn were being formed on a potter's wheel. Still faster, and a whirling dervish of gas. Now the subcloud spreads and flattens until an equilibrium is reached and it assumes a shape.

This event would certainly be celebrated if there were a race of beings sufficiently cosmopolitan to look at things intergalactically. A flat disc with a bulge at the center and arms beginning to form, a new celestial object rising in a great new dawn. A bloom, a flower stretching roots and tendrils into space as if it finds nourishment in the thin substance there. Order established in the very midst of chaos, in disorder and the void. A spiral thing suspended in space, fluttering like a victory banner. The first and most immense of a series of patterns, the mark of a process that continues in us and will continue beyond us. A spiral, the Milky Way. As far as our kind is concerned, the universe has come into being.

From a broader point of view, this is one of many local births. The original cloud gave rise to a whole family of galaxies, the two biggest being our Milky Way and another spiral system known as Andromeda, or M31 for short. The family also includes the Large and Small Magellanic Clouds, which are among the unshaped irregulars; M33, a galaxy in the constellation Triangulum; and some very small and very dim galaxies in the constellations Draco and Fornax and Sculptor. We know that the parent cloud produced at least nineteen offspring and there may be others too faint to see. They have remained together as a close-knit group ever since the beginning, held by mutually attracting gravitational forces. Our local cluster of galaxies occupies a region about thirty-three million light-years in diameter, with the Milky Way and Andromeda lying opposite one another at the extreme edges.

Larger families born out of more extensive clouds fly like great flocks in the distance. In the direction of the constellation of Virgo, more than three hundred million light-years away, is a many-membered cluster containing at least a thousand galaxies. This family includes an overgrown and restive globular galaxy. It has an enormous blue jet rushing across its center and emits intense static, radio waves powerful enough to be picked up by special receiving sets on earth. Beyond that we see the Ursa Major cluster, which has hundreds of members and may be observed through a stellar window, the bowl of the Big Dipper. Still further, at the outermost limits of our observing power, where the telescope on Palomar Mountain can barely detect it, is an unnamed cluster three billion light-years or more distant. Its galaxies appear as faint gray spots on photographic plates, and yet many of them may be systems as vast and densely populated as the Milky Way.

Clusters are observed on all horizons in the skies, suggesting that our mathematics has served us well. In certain basic respects at least, the theory of a fragmenting cloud, or some similar splitting-up process, seems to represent what actually happened. A type of chain reaction could have been responsible for the existence of families of galaxies, for the creation on a large scale of bursts of galaxies within a relatively short period. As if seeds were scattered in a field and grew into plants on the same acres and all at about the same time. Perhaps an appreciable proportion of galaxies are well-adjusted members of clusters, or were at one time. Some of the galaxies that move separate and alone may have broken away from their family groups when they were younger.

Island systems and archipelagos, born in showers, receding at greater and greater velocities in an expanding universe. The galaxy which comprises our back yard, the spiral Milky Way, happens to be one of the biggest. It is the first of the long-enduring patterns whose origins we are considering, the first of many beginnings. Its history is our main concern because we are part of it and in it and know it best. But there is no reason to rule out analogous evolutions in other galaxies. We may assume that the coming of patterns, the shaping of increasingly complex patterns, is not a local phenomenon—but a mark of the trend of things throughout the universe, everywhere.

The Lights
Come On
3

SOMETHING else begins to happen in the cloud fragment, even before it whips itself into a spiral. When it is still an irregular mass, just starting to spin, the skies are still unimaginably dark. We are parasites of light and would shrivel in blackness that lasted too long. Power lines break, electricity fails for a night or two, and already we are ill at ease. We feel a discomfort as physical as if we were living in dampness or breathing stale air. The need for light is almost as primitive as the need for food.

Imagine the light fading every day after sunset, the way it was in the caves before fire when men first learned to fear darkness. Imagine no sun at all and utter darkness all the time. It is like this everywhere in that part of the original cloud which will become the Milky Way. The shapeless gas begins to pull itself together, tightens and contracts and spins faster, takes on the vague outlines of a shape, a sphere-like thing. A whirling prelude. The first act is under way.

And now a darkness older than time comes to an end. There are lights, primeval lights, glowworm lights in a forest of space. Not many and not bright, to start with. Faint and flickering and lonely, like the lights of fishing boats in a Mediterranean bay seen from high above. We move up front, taking a place close to a scene of action where the stuff of the universe is simmering and where one of the early lights is about to appear.

The process we see is familiar in certain respects. First it was the original cloud, the raw material for many future galaxies, which began to evolve. Then fragments of the cloud, each a galaxy in the making, broke away and launched a number of parallel evolutions. Now a bit of one of the fragments breaks away, a fragment of a fragment, yet vast by noncosmic standards. This particle is hundreds of thousands of light-years across and contains billions and billions and billions of tons of matter. Another step in a hierarchy of splitting substance.

The clump of gas contracts like a deflating bladder with the air being forced out. Faster and faster at first, as if it would collapse into a small solid ball. But little by little, as the clump evolves from formlessness to a nebulous globe, the shrinking loses momentum and slows down. Then deep inside the globe, like a bulb in a great lamp, a core begins to glow. The gas stops contracting, expands a bit, contracts again. The glow becomes dimmer, brighter, dimmer, and so on. We are reminded of throbbing and pulsing things, heartbeats or breathing rhythms. A series of rapid and shorter and shorter tremors which die out like the vibrations of a tuning fork, or an echo losing itself in the hills. The globe has stopped shuddering. It is a star now, shining and shining steadily.

It floats, like a balloon or a lone buoy in a wide, wide sea. It burns bright, an incandescent compromise between two powerful and opposing forces. One force, the force of gravitation, dominated during the early, fast-shrinking stage. But a counterforce was building up. Gases trapped at the core of the contracting protostar began to become warm, and warm gases tend to expand. The outward pressure, weak at first, grew as shrinking continued and internal temperatures rose. Until the struggle was joined in earnest. The contraction slowed and, after a brief tug-of-war, stopped. The end came when temperatures had risen sufficiently so that the core "caught fire." Hydrogen gas started burning in a controlled nuclear reaction.

Now the metabolism of the star is neatly adjusted in a natural playing off of force against force. The star has settled down for the long haul. If it contracts further, temperature and gas pressure at the core rise, tending to expand the star and restore its appropriate dimensions. If things start swinging in the other direction, if the star expands too much, the internal temperature falls and the outward pressure of gases falls too and there is a compensating contraction. A floating valve. A system in balance, but precariously so. This pattern endures and develops on the very edge of annihilation. Never far from chaos, wavering all the time between extremes, between explosion and collapse.

The birth of a very early star, one of the first lights that appear as the Milky Way forms. More lights come later, many of them in clusters on the edges of the globular galaxy and also in the galactic center. And still more lights, like a display heralding a festival or an Illumination Night in space. The galaxy flattens and approaches a spiral pattern, and spins and spins. The splitting process that breeds stars is accelerating. Within the spinning system, within the whirlpool, a multitude of coiling places. A mosaic of smaller eddies, entire broods and flurries of smaller eddies, billions of bright, spinning spheres. Smaller whirlpools within a whirlpool, and a shower of stars.

This is a spiral dawn, the early morning of the Milky Way. A large-scale version of what happens on cool crisp mornings when air, heavy with moisture gathered during the night, climbs along the crests of little hills, and spills over into the fields—and condenses and sprinkles bright droplets on grass and leaves and spider webs. The first bursts of light, a dew of stars.

The oldest stars of our galaxy began shining about seven billion years ago, in times more unsettled than the present. The thunders and lightnings and typhoons in the Milky Way were far more violent than they are now. Ancient stars still show signs of having been born among upheavals and turbulences. They still move at high velocities, up to 360,000 miles an hour, as the result of forces applied to them eons and eons ago. In those wildest of times, perhaps thirty billion stars came into being within a rather short interval, galactically speaking—about five hundred million years. Since then there have been more stars, another seventy billion. A brave new galaxy of stars, globes poised and hovering in delicate balance like beautiful colored bubbles.

Now, long after the beginning, we look at the stars and try to understand how they developed and what will happen to them. Our natural senses are not sufficient for the task. All stars but the sun, even the nearest viewed through the finest telescopes in the world, appear merely as specks, white spots on photographic film. Except for the sun, no man has ever seen a star as anything else, and in the absence of interstellar space travel, no man ever will. For the time being we must rely on the laws of physics, and on the increasingly refined instruments which we keep devising to see what the unaided eye cannot see. And for the time being that may prove sufficient.

A cold clear night on the top of Palomar Mountain, excellent conditions for all-night viewing and long time exposures. Such conditions occur only once or twice every two weeks or so, and every moment is doubly valuable. The 200-inch telescope, a skyscraper on bearings, focuses on a position in space—a faint target. Photographs reveal a star in that position and indicate a precise latitude and longitude. But if you looked through the telescope, you would see nothing. The star is too faint to see. It is not very bright and lies more than three thousand light-years away. What starlight there is passes through a pinpoint hole in a diaphragm covering the telescopic lens, an opening less than one twenty-fifth of an inch in diameter.

The telescope is being used as a great funnel to gather and concentrate light for another instrument. Radiation from the star falls on a special sensing device called a photoelectric multiplier or "electric eye"—an instrument used early in World War II to help jam enemy radar signals, and now modified for more basic purposes. An astronomer is busy keeping tabs on things: "You have to follow the telescope all the time." He makes the thousand and one adjustments necessary to obtain precise measurements of the apparent brightness or magnitude of a star only one-fortieth as bright as the night sky which includes it. These measurements will be used to calculate how rapidly the star produces energy, and perhaps how long it will shine.

The setting of a four-position light filter—red, yellow, blue, ultraviolet—is changed at regular intervals to gauge the color of the star. Color is a mark of temperature. Yellow flames burn at a higher level than red flames, and different stars have different colors which indicate increasing surface temperatures: from red at the "cool" end of the scale to orange, yellow, white, blue-white. Knowing the color and thus the surface temperature of the star, one can then compute temperatures at the interior. Color may also provide clues to its mass.

One night and hours spent observing one star. The record is being written automatically in the form of inked lines on

COLOR MAGNITUDE RECORD OF A STAR

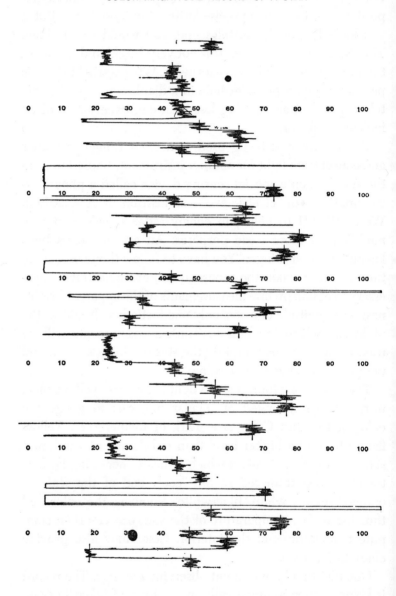

moving chart paper, and the chart may be many feet long before the night is over. It used to take about four days to analyze the photoelectric observations of a single night. Now, with the aid of another electronic instrument, a high-speed calculating machine, the entire job can be done in an hour or so—a speed-up of nearly a hundred times, the difference between a century and a year.

But even this speed-up is not enough under present conditions. The data keep accumulating. Other stars in the same general region of the sky have already written their signatures during previous nights, and more signatures are yet to come. Roll after roll of chart paper, facts piling up too swiftly to handle. For there is a shortage of electronic help. The time of the robot computer is scheduled months in advance to work for investigators in other fields, and astronomy must wait its turn. So the records pile up. And in between chores the investigator at the telescope speaks wistfully about one of his dream plans—an Institute for Theoretical Astronomy which would house, among other things, calculating machines to work full time on the stars.

Tonight all the observations, all the charts, are part of a color-magnitude survey of one cluster, one colony of stars all formed together in a single burst at roughly the same time. And this survey itself is only part of a comprehensive program of surveys involving many other clusters. A sampling program, a poll conducted on a large scale, which fits in with and supplements an enormous amount of other information—and helps astronomers obtain a fuller understanding of the lives of the stars.

The task has been exceedingly difficult, and the wonder is that we know as much as we do. Our lives are so short in comparison with the lives of stars that, in effect, we see hardly anything at all in the process of becoming. In effect, we have a huge and growing file of photographs, static pictures of a few stars among the hundred billion stars of the

Milky Way. We must arrange these pictures in a sequence that makes sense. It is something like receiving a hundred motion-picture frames, single pictures cut at random from a two-hour, feature-length film—and then being asked to deduce the entire plot.

Imagine attempting to deduce human life cycles under analogous circumstances. You belong to an utterly different breed of beings, and you have no direct knowledge of human development—no detailed, step-by-step evidence of birth or adolescence of middle age or senility. Your own natural life span is far too brief compared with human longevities. In fact, you have only about thirty seconds to live and you can draw on records accumulated during a past which amounts to little more than half an hour. (Actually, the records that help you most go back little more than four minutes.)

You see people at great distances through a permanent haze. They come in different sizes and shapes and colors, and move at different rates in different ways. You must figure out everything for yourself, and be extremely careful about what you take for granted. You have no right to assume, without first-rate evidence, that a small crawling pinkish object is the precursor of something else—that it will grow into, or has any basic relationship with, that larger object which moves about on two legs. The sequence might be the other way around, or the two objects might represent entirely different species.

Exploring the Milky Way is one long chain of similar problems. In a general way it is evident that the stars, like all patterns we know of, are changing, and changing according to physical laws. Philosophers and astronomers thought otherwise not long ago. It was natural to speak of the eternal stars, just as poets speak of eternal hills and eternal cities. And if hills and cities can seem unchanging, how much more the stars which are so remote and so long-lived.

46

Yet things do change, and the way they change is becoming clearer. The evidence is taking shape, a complex and continually developing network of interrelated facts and interpretations of facts and theories. Piecing together many many observations relevant to the ages of clusters. Thus a dense group of stars located above the disk of the Milky Way and well outside the central bulge probably formed when the galaxy was still a globe and was left hanging outside as the system flattened. Astronomers use a variety of techniques to measure the masses and sizes and energy production of different stars in clusters believed to be of different ages.

Think of the body of astronomical knowledge as a variety of abstract or symbolic organism—and yet a thing that feeds on new findings and grows and develops quite as definitely as any real-life organism. Knowledge, in other words, has a biology of its own, an embryology and growth pattern and evolution—even a system of waste disposal, as faulty observations and inadequate theories are discarded. Every new fact crosschecks and in some way modifies the complex web of pre-existing facts. No single observation, no single finding, settles anything. Instead it feeds into and becomes part of the deepening pool of knowledge. It follows that we are considerably wiser today than we were even as recently as one or two decades ago. It also follows that much of what we observe continues to baffle us, and that in a few decades many of our notions about the universe will be quite different from what they are today.

But the broad outlines of a new and more sophisticated picture are emerging, and here is how stellar evolution appears to be unfolding. We start in an old cluster of the Milky Way, and follow the careers of representative stars. The early population will include members having a wide range of masses, which also means that they will have different colors. For example, an unusually massive blob of gas possesses a correspondingly powerful gravitational field—

that is, it has a very strong tendency to contract. Establishing internal pressures strong enough to counteract this tendency calls for extra-high temperatures in the blue range. So massive protostars are likely to develop into hot, blue stars. Stars formed out of lesser amounts of gas achieve a balancing of forces at lower temperatures and may have cooler, redder colors.

Massive stars live dangerously. They come into being with more than their share of substance, in the most extreme cases enough substance to make nearly a hundred stars like the sun, and burn their candles at both ends. A heavyweight may condense from its gas cloud rapidly, sometimes within ten thousand to a hundred thousand years. Then it emits its hot, bright blue or blue-white light. This distinctive color marks a period of settling down and relatively stable fuel burning, of quiet domestication. It does not last long. After a few million years the star becomes restless, begins heaving—and then inflates considerably. The temperature drops during the expansion and the color changes from blue to white to yellow to orange to red. The star is now a red giant.

The fact that massive blue stars have rapid careers accounts for an interesting observation. Relatively young clusters include a large proportion of such stars, as might be expected. But the populations of old clusters are quite different. They show a complete and significant lack of very hot, very blue stars. In other words, stars which shone blue in the early days are blue no longer, having long since burned themselves out and changed to cooler, redder and less luminous bodies.

But it takes all kinds of stars to make a galaxy. Less massive stars formed in old Milky Way clusters live more leisurely and more conservative lives. Among them are yellow stars with masses equal to one or two suns. Having less substance to start with, they are geared to a slower pace and use their natural resources sparingly. The infancy of such a star, the stage from unformed gas cloud to steadily burning furnace, may last some fifty million years or more—and during the same period a blue star may race through its entire active life. A yellow star of intermediate mass, a star like our sun, undergoes little change for ten to twelve billion years. After that it also follows the course that a blue star must follow, although more slowly. It also expands to a red giant.

The red-giant stage is not the last stage, either for these stars or for heavyweights. In all cases the declining stars ultimately shrink to much smaller dimensions and end up as bodies containing only about as much mass as the sun. That means they must discard large quantities of matter somewhere along the line. Take the comparatively mild case of a red giant having only twice as much material as the sun. In the process of reducing down to weight it must get rid of half its substance, the equivalent of one solar mass—and one solar mass is two times 10^{27}, or two billion billion billion, tons.

Stars go through considerable exertion as they proceed to strip themselves down to size. The full details of what they do, and in what order, remain a dark family secret. It is as if you were reading a detective story, came to a crucial point, and then discovered that fifty pages were missing just before the final chapters of the book. A serious gap in the stellar story comes after the red-giant stage, although certain observations suggest the sort of thing that is going on.

Part of the evidence for the reducing process, for the shedding of abundant quantities of matter, comes from double-star systems. Such systems consist of two stars bound together by mutual gravitational attraction, and revolving about each other as satellites. Certain peculiar conditions have been observed in systems where one of the pair is a red giant. Its companion is partly obscured by a haze of fast-moving gases, and it appears that the haze consists of material ejected by the giant itself.

49

Some red giants, at least, seem to be spouting off substance like geysers. Perhaps the effect can be traced to turbulence in the lower atmosphere of such a star. Violent motions could produce a kind of blast at the depths, a shock that forces matter together suddenly and creates a "thickened" zone for a fraction of a second. Then the energy passes from lower to higher parts of the atmosphere, upward through less and less dense regions, in the form of a mammoth ripple or compression wave. As the wave rises, the movement of gases at higher and higher levels becomes faster and faster until the speed exceeds a certain limit—and an enormous blob of gas breaks away.

The process is something like the cracking of a whip. A flick of the thick, heavy end starts a wave of energy which is transmitted faster and faster to the very thin, light end. The tip of the whip accelerates to supersonic velocities and breaks the sound barrier with a loud bang. In the case of a red giant, the tail of the whip comes off and is hurled out into space. The whip-cracking theory has not yet been proved or disproved. But we do know for a fact that compression waves with the required energy could be produced in the lower atmospheres of red giants.

Other stars seem to be ejecting matter in different ways, and under different conditions. Photographs taken through a powerful telescope show peculiar nebulae, masses of gas which look remarkably like living cells. A typical specimen is egg-shaped, about a third of a light-year across, and consists of a large dark nucleus surrounded by a glowing cloud or halo. The object responsible for all the trouble is a bright star embedded in the center of the nucleus. This star rotates and sprays out material like a garden sprinkler, and the halo around it is that material in the form of a vast shell. Such nebulae will probably fade and be dispersed in a few thousand years, but new ones keep coming and keep pumping substance into interstellar space. Another type of star may

LIFE HISTORY OF AVERAGE-SIZE STAR

gas condenses to...

...star and solar system

after
about
ten
to
twelve
billion
years,...
star
expands
to
red giant...

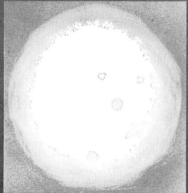

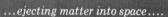
...ejecting matter into space....

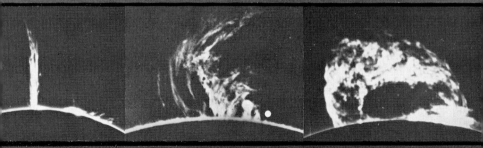

...and
eventually
dying
off
to the black dwarf stage

IDENTIFYING TECHNETIUM ON A STAR

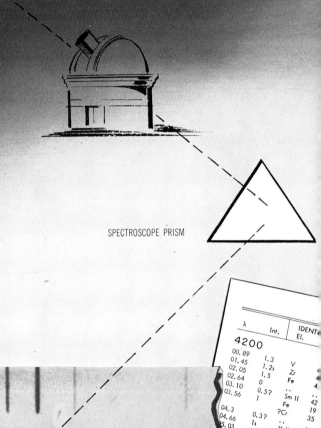

PULSATING STAR—
R ANDROMEDAE 00838

SPECTROSCOPE PRISM

stellar spectrum (actual)

Fe arc

R And

↑ 4238.21 ANGSTROM UNITS

laboratory spectrum (schematic)

↓ 4238.19 ANGSTROM UNITS

Spectral line of technetium,
observed in laboratory, matches
previously unidentified spectral
line from R Andromedae

λ	Int.	IDENT El.	
4200			
00.89	1.3	V	
01.45	1.2s	Zr	
02.05	1.5	Fe	4
02.64	0		4
03.10	0.5?		42
03.56	1	Sm II	
		Fe	19
04.3	0.3?	?Cr	35
04.66	1s		
5.03	0.8	Y II	1
5.29	0.3	Eu II	1
68	0.4		
	0.5	?Nd II	19
	3.5	?Sm II	38
	1w	Fe	3
05	0.4w		
09.89			
10.38	2		
11.34	1	V	24
11.74		Fe	152
	0.5	Zr	.35
13.88		Dy	1.8*
15.44	1.5	Ti	.72
16.07	10	Zr	279
	6	Sr II	45
26.7		Fe	1
	3		.52
32.6	50		.19
34.01	0.5	Ca	2
	0.7	Fe	.73
34.55	1	Co	3
		V	6
		V	3
35.88	1.5w	Sm II	42
		Zr	0.6*
		Y II	5
36.57	1	Y	.73
37.07		Fe	.94
38.20	0.3	?Zr II	152
38.90	1.4	Fe	110
39.32	0	Tc	19
39.86	2	Fe	0.0*
40.36	0.7	Zr	693
41.20	2	Fe	45
		Zr	18

CREATION OF ELEMENTS IN THE STARS

FIRST GENERATION STARS

million degrees

...*condense out of pure hydrogen clouds...
steady burning...groups of four hydrogen
nuclei built into helium nuclei
(hydrogen 1 ⟶ helium 4)*

llion to
on degrees

...*red giant stage...
helium nuclei built into heavier elements:
carbon 12, oxygen 16, neon 20, up to iron
group (atomic weight, about 56)*

...*newly created elements
scattered into space
by ejection or explosion*

SECOND GENERATION STARS

...*condense out of
hydrogen clouds plus
carbon, oxygen, neon,
and heavier elements
produced in first
generation stars*

...*red giant stage...
neutron reactions
produce heavier
elements including
technetium 99, gold 197,
lead 207, bismuth 209*

...*supernova explosions
produce heaviest
radioactive elements
including radium 226,
uranium 238,
californium 254*

20 billion degrees

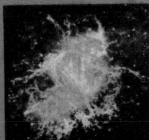

THIRD GENERATION STARS
LIKE OUR SUN

...*condense out of
hydrogen clouds which
now contain all known
elements*

SHAPING OF EARTH AND SOLAR SYSTEM

*interstellar cloud condenses,
forming core (raw material of sun)
surrounded by nebula of unused
gases (raw material of planets).*

*System spins faster and faster
nebula flattens, density in
nebula increases.*

Vortices form in nebula.

*Crystalline particles
form in vortices
and
fuse
together
into
larger
and
larger
masses,
producing planets...*

EARTH

flare up in a grand outburst, and become tens of thousands of times brighter for a week or two. It may expel an average of 100,000,000,000,000,000 tons of matter every second before it calms down completely, and drifts further toward its old age.

By far the most energetic stellar performer is the exploding star or supernova. Indeed, few phenomena in the universe are more violent, except perhaps for something like the original explosion which may have launched the expanding universe—and we are not at all certain whether that hypothetical cataclysm actually occurred. But we are certain about exploding stars, because we can see the material scattered by some of them. One supernova burst more than nine hundred years ago, appropriately enough on the Fourth of July. Chinese astronomers saw it, and Navaho Indians in the deserts of northern Arizona may have seen it too.

A carving on a rocky wall in Navaho Canyon shows a huge body near the crescent moon, in just about the position where the supernova would have appeared before dawn on the morning of July 5, 1054. Today the debris of that explosion forms a body called the Crab Nebula. It includes filaments of gas ejected at speeds so high that they are still traveling two and a half million miles an hour. At the center of the nebula, like a jewel in a wad of cotton, is an important and rarely observed type of star—a very small white object, the late stage of what may have been a fast-living blue heavyweight.

Such stars are called white dwarfs. Astronomers have come to recognize them as telltale signs of advanced evolution for all stars that pass through the red-giant stage. Some stars travel the road from giant to dwarf without making much fuss; others are violent, like the supernovae. But terrific disruptions in the skies occur rarely, and we have not yet observed a much-studied and familiar star in the act of exploding. (The odds are that we shall have to wait a few hundred

51

million years for that.) So the place of cataclysm in the lives of the stars is still more theory than fact. The general course of events, however, is reasonably clear. Most stars discard substance and pass through the white-dwarf stage on their way to extinction.

White dwarfs are matter in a highly concentrated state. The smallest are even smaller than the earth, and since their masses are about that of the sun, they are the densest objects known. The average white dwarf is so compact at the center that one cubic foot of its substance, about enough to fill a hat-box, would weigh considerably more than the ocean liner "United States." Although only two hundred or so white dwarfs have been observed, it has been estimated that the Milky Way contains some five billion. This is about one out of every twenty stars in our galaxy, and indicates the proportion which have passed their prime.

The final stage of a star's career may last many billions of years. It fades like a dying flower and color changes signify the slow and inevitable flowing away of heat. A white dwarf cools to yellow, orange, red, and finally sputters out completely. Stellar corpses are black dwarfs, the end of the road. There are probably none of them yet in the Milky Way, because our galaxy is not old enough to have utterly dead stars. And even if they did exist we could not see them, for they emit no light. But for all stars, sooner or later, the future is black.

Incidentally, we must not forget the most long-lived stars of all. These red bodies were born small and cool, and except for getting born, they have done practically nothing since the formation of the Milky Way. They contain less material than the sun to start with, and hence need to discard little if any of it as they grow older. They are slowpokes with a vengeance. In fact, if you are looking for a Rock of Ages in the universe—for something that will endure practically unaltered in the midst of cosmic upheavals—choose the smallest and the coolest of these stars. It will die when its time comes. But it will probably not have changed noticeably a thousand billion years from now, when most of the stars in today's skies will differ radically from their present states.

So much for the dying of individual stars, the trail from giant to dwarf. The chapter could end at this point if it were not for discoveries of the last twenty years or less. But today we know that dying is only part of the story, and perhaps the least important part. Furthermore, when it comes to the future of stellar populations as a whole, we lean heavily on speculation. The speculation will come in a later chapter. Right now, here in the Milky Way, processes are under way which indicate that the galaxy, at least in its present stage, is more than a place of stars in their declining twilight years.

A photograph taken at the Lick Observatory in January 1947 shows three stars, dark blurs in a very small region of the Orion Nebula. Three stars in a nest of thick interstellar gas and dust. Seven years later another photograph of the same region, taken at the same observatory, shows two additional stars which did not appear in the earlier picture and must have increased in brightness by at least fifteen to twenty times. Two objects only a fraction of an inch apart on the photographic plate, but hundreds of millions of miles apart in the skies. Newly born stars, or stars that existed before and simply flared into visibility? Some astronomers believe the bodies are indeed new, and if this diagnosis is correct, the photographs represent our first direct record of the birth of stars.

In any case, other evidence leaves no doubt that stars are being created, many of them in the Orion Nebula—and all of them in regions rich in gas and dust. The Milky Way contains a large number of nebulae, perhaps as many as ten thousand, sufficiently dense to give rise to infant stars. Bright blue and blue-white stars, the sort which will rush through life and which are no longer found in the oldest clusters of the Milky

Way. Stars so hot and burning so swiftly that they must have been created only yesterday in stellar terms, a few hundred thousand to a few million years ago.

Stars that breed stars. A blue-hot heavyweight "boils" the tangle of gases out of which it is born. The heat drives the gases away at enormous speeds, creating an expanding shell —the advancing front of a spherical shock wave. The shell collides with cool gases and compresses them, and along the boundaries of the collision more new stars may condense. Another chain reaction, another shower of stars in many colors and sizes. Because of such processes, birth rates still exceed death rates in the Milky Way. Every year, on the average, one star becomes a white dwarf. During the same period three to four brand-new blue, yellow, orange and red stars come into being, forming out of available interstellar gases.

A galaxy is almost organic in its development. In the beginning stars form out of a matrix of gases, and the gases are used up for the making of many stars. Then the stars fade and, while they fade, lose part of their substance, which returns to the great interstellar pool of gases. The used or ejected material, together with material that has not yet gone into star-building, is incorporated into "second-generation" stars. The cycle is probably repeating itself, and stars being born today probably represent later generations. The Milky Way is like a garden where many flowers wither and bloom —and where withering and blooming, in seasonal rhythms, make up the cycles which keep things alive and stirring.

The Creation

of Elements

4

THE Milky Way, a galaxy among galaxies, a vast disc swimming and spinning in a sea of thin gas. A flat island world where a billion miles or a billion tons may be nothing in particular, where time falls away precipitously and without limit, like the walls of a bottomless abyss. A skyful of colored spheres, luminous bodies moving in splendor and living their lives in the grand manner. Evolution out in the open for all to see, events accessible to direct observation.

Meanwhile, concurrent, a less prominent evolution. Cycles of star deaths and star births, exploding stars and flaring stars and steady burners, protostars and giants and dwarfs—all these things reflect an unfolding of events which we cannot observe directly. Events in little, seething and restlessness in submicroscopic worlds. Invisible atomic events. Like celebrities, the stars have no privacy. Men have watched and wondered at their comings and goings for more than half a million years; poets sing often of the stars. Atoms are less evident and less widely sung.

Another evolution, or, rather, part of the same fundamental process that shapes the most massive and the least massive bodies in the universe. Elements are created inside growing stars, more than ninety species of atoms which occur naturally and which in various combinations make up all other substances from water to crystal to protoplasm itself. Stars and atoms taking form at the same time, a symphony of evolving matter. The stars are the big sounds, the drum rolls and the trumpet blasts and the crashing of cymbals. And in the background a theme of atoms like a tune played high and soft and steady underneath the big sounds, as it were, and woven through them.

It is not easy, gathering evidence for creation. Our notions about the synthesis of elements depend on disciplined and often tedious accumulations of data. Precision is as important as inspiration. In 1944, on Mount Wilson overlooking Los Angeles, an astronomer studies R Andromedae 001838, a pulsing star which brightens and fades at regular intervals like a lighthouse beacon. The astronomer is not using an electric eye, because he wants to do more than measure the predominating color of the star. The problem is to analyze a wide range of the detectable radiations it emits, and the instrument for that purpose is the spectroscope.

The light from R Andromedae, like the light from all stars, is a mixture of a large number of wave lengths or colors—and each color identifies one form of a specific element in the atmosphere of the star. For example, the atmosphere contains calcium atoms, and these particles emit radiations including a reddish light with a wave length of 6439.1 angstrom units (an angstrom unit is about four billionths of an inch). The light travels in all directions through space, and some of it, after a trip of many years, obligingly enters the lenses of the spectroscope—scrambled together with all the other wave lengths emitted by all the other kinds of atoms in the atmosphere of R Andromedae.

The spectroscope is an unscrambling device. The star's light, a composite of wave lengths representing the identifying signals of many different atoms, passes through a prism. The prism splits the light into a kind of rainbow spectrum. The mixed wave lengths are separated one from the other, so that the jumble of signals becomes a set of discrete signals. All the information is recorded on photographic plates—two or three plates, each exposed for two hours—and appears as a series of alternate dark and light bands which resemble the rungs of a ladder and represent different wave lengths.

Then the work really begins, the detail really piles up. The astronomer examines the bands on the plates, one by one, under a special measuring microscope, and makes calculation after calculation, and the job takes about three months even with the help of a full-time assistant. Eventually a table is published, eight to ten pages of fine print, columns and rows of numbers, the first of several tables. A typical line: "5474.23—1—Ti—108—0.23." The data indicate among other things that the atmosphere of the remote giant star R Andromedae contains atoms of the metal titanium, a fact deduced from the presence in the spectrum of a dark line at the position representing a wave length of 5474.23 angstrom units, a characteristic titanium signal. The table contains somewhere between one thousand and two thousand such lines. Some of the lines have blank spaces. The symbol for the element is missing, indicating that the nature of the signaling atoms is not known.

This project starts in 1944. About six years later a physicist in Washington receives a speck of material, a tiny fraction of an ounce of a rare element called technetium. The element does not exist naturally on the earth. The sample comes from the Atomic Energy Commission, having been produced artificially in nuclear furnaces. The physicist burns and vaporizes the sample in a hot carbon arc, changing it to a gas. Under such conditions its atoms emit their characteristic wave lengths. The spectrum of technetium includes a wave length of 4238.19 angstrom units, a color in the blue-violet range. The physicist writes a paper, sending a prepublication copy to California. The astronomer goes back to his table of spectral lines for R Andromedae—and finds a blank space, an unidentified wave length of 4238.21 angstrom units. A stellar signal with almost the exact wave length as the one observed on earth, in the Washington laboratory. Off by only two-hundredths of a unit, about one two-thousandth of one percent. A gap in the table is filled. Sufficient precision to identify technetium in the star. Nature has vaporized the element in her own carbon arcs on R Andromedae. The experiments check, and there is more evidence. Unidentified wave lengths are found in the spectra of other stars, tables are examined and brought up to date. The result: one more finding and an exciting conclusion about the creation of elements.

Now and then in science, not frequently, a single fact discovered at the right time is particularly rich in implications. It reverberates, in a sense. There are overtones of meaning, so that a full interpretation yields surprisingly deep insights. Such a fact is the discovery of technetium in the atmospheres of certain stars. It happens that the atoms of the element are unstable. They split spontaneously and, in terms of stellar longevities, swiftly. For example, a population originally made up of ten billion atoms of the slowest-decaying form of technetium will probably contain about half that number of atoms in 200,000 years. And the death rate continues, with the population dwindling to one-quarter, one-eighth, one-sixteenth of its former total in successive 200,000-year periods.

So the presence of large numbers of technetium atoms in a star which may be billions of years old indicates that there are births as well as deaths. Atomic populations are being replenished. Technetium not only exists in the stars, but is also being created in the stars. This conclusion in itself is sufficient to disprove the notion that all the elements were created long ago in one fell swoop. Proponents of the cosmic-egg hypothesis, the hypothesis that the expanding universe came into being with the explosion of a superdense mass of matter, once believed that all the elements were formed in the first twenty minutes or so after the explosion—"in less time than it takes to cook roast duck and potatoes." That belief is no longer valid.

Even more important conclusions follow from the discovery of technetium in the stars. This is a heavy element. Its longest-lived form weighs 99 units on the atomic scale—that is, 99 times the weight of an atom of hydrogen, the simplest and lightest element. For several reasons it is convenient to assume that in the beginning the cloud which turned into the Milky Way was pure hydrogen, or almost entirely pure hydrogen. If so, there is no way to go from hydrogen to technetium in a single jump.

You have to go by easy stages, step by step. To build a sky-scraper manv previously manufactured parts are required— steel girders and slabs of stone and concrete and insulating materials and other products used in the final assembly. Similarly the building of heavy atoms involves a long series of preliminary steps and simpler, lighter atoms. Biology provides an analogy which is perhaps more pertinent. At one time presumably no living things were to be found on earth, and terrestrial matter consisted of relatively simple compounds. At a later date swarms of cells existed in primeval waters.

But full-fledged cells did not arise suddenly out of simple compounds. An enormous amount of preliminary organization took place, the evolving of long-chain molecules and coiled molecules and membranes and a great many other elaborately interwoven materials. Technetium also represents

59

one result of an evolution, a long building-up process. It implies the gradual synthesis of other elements, transmutations on a scale beyond the fantasies of the alchemists.

There was evidence for synthesis before the identification of R Andromedae signals, and much new evidence has accumulated since then. But the finding helped put things in sharp focus. It brought science face to face with a significant fact. It was a green light for continued research. It told investigators, in effect: "All right—now you know for certain that at least one of the heavy elements is being created in stars. Your basic problem from here on is to discover how."

Astronomers are attacking the problem. They have joined forces with physicists who study the nucleus of the atom, a pursuit which few laymen took seriously before World War II. Not long before the war a popular American comedian conducted an interview with an actor playing the role of a nuclear physicist. The comedian's last question: "Professor, could you tell us just why you spend your time smashing atoms?" The "professor" hemmed and hawed, and finally blurted, "Well, some day someone might want half an atom." That remark brought down the house, but it does not seem quite as funny today.

Our nuclear weapons and nuclear power plants are by-products of basic research on the very heart of the atom. Another by-product of this research is new knowledge about the lives of stars, and the physical processes of creation. Stellar evolution, stellar metabolism, is a story of the fusing and splitting of atoms in natural nuclear furnaces. Furthermore, powerful machines designed to bombard atoms make many things possible. With them we can study, in earthbound laboratories, processes that may be taking place deep inside stars of our galaxy and inside stars of galaxies scattered throughout the universe.

To follow such processes we go back to the beginning again, to the great cloud which gave rise to the Milky Way and its cluster of galaxies. We have good reason to believe that element-building has been under way for billions of years—and still, after all that time, more than ninety percent of all the atoms in today's universe are hydrogen atoms. The cloud is extremely thin. On the average, any given hydrogen atom lies about a yard or so from its nearest neighbor, and a yard represents an enormous distance in comparison with the size of these atoms. They are like two small BB-shots separated by five hundred billion miles. Obviously, neighbors in this world have little to do with one another.

Isolation is peaceful but it does not last. The force of gravitation goes to work and the contractions start. The original cloud shrinks and breaks into smaller clouds, which shrink further as they approach galactic dimensions. And within one of the smaller clouds, the forming Milky Way, many lesser clouds appear—broods of embryonic stars, shrinking still more as they spin. By this time atoms are hermits no longer. Indeed, overcrowding has become intolerable and there is no such thing as privacy. Here is the situation for an early middleweight star in the process of contracting: In the star, a volume about the size of a telephone booth now houses as many atoms as were once housed in a volume large enough to hold several thousand suns.

The star continues to deflate and the temperature rises, particularly in central regions. Particles buzz with activity. Normally, a hydrogen atom consists of two subparticles—a proton at the center and a lighter electron moving outside the proton nucleus. But hemmed-in hydrogen atoms at the interior of the star lose their electrons, and go about in the form of "bare" protons or nuclei. As the temperature increases, they move faster and faster, as if attempting to escape. Speeds of thousands of miles a minute and yet, even under such hectic and crowded conditions, the particles rarely come into contact with one another. Communications are still poor.

Protons have a sort of built-in aloofness, a tendency to keep their distance. They carry positive electrical charges, and particles with the same sort of charge, like the north poles of electromagnets, repel one another vigorously. If you have two sufficiently strong magnets and move the north poles toward one another, you find yourself exerting more and more effort as they approach one another. In a while you reach a point where all your strength is not enough to bring them closer. You might decide to use a machine from this point on, a giant vise that would force the reluctant north poles together. If so, you had better hide behind a thick concrete wall. Sooner or later the forces of repulsion become so enormous that the machine or the magnets shatter and there is a burst of jagged steel shrapnel.

An analogous situation prevails inside our early-type star. Protons in the star, positively charged hydrogen nuclei, also resist close approaches up to a point—and that point is crucial. There is a "breaking" point, a point at which resistance collapses suddenly and abruptly and completely. From time to time two protons approach each other with velocities sufficiently great to bring them within about one ten-trillionth of an inch from one another. This is a collision. The next step may be the collapse, and the particles fuse to form a single tightly welded, double-weight nucleus. It is all or nothing. Utter aloofness or, if that fails, swift union.

The odds against union are terrific. Collisions take place so rarely in the core of our star that the average proton may whiz about for hundreds of millions of years among swarms of fellow hot-rodders before becoming involved in a serious traffic accident. And even then there may be no union. The encounter is brief, so brief that the blink of an eyelid or the leap of a tiger is an eternity by comparison, and nothing dramatic may happen. Only one out of more than a thousand billion billion collisions results in a double-weight nucleus.

Such is the magnitude of the odds against creation. A gambler unfamiliar with anything more than these facts would not think twice about how to place his bets. Charged particles are certainly reluctant joiners. But he would lose his money. The star contains so many protons, and conditions are so crowded and dynamic, that improbabilities become not only probable but inevitable. The odds against being dealt thirteen spades in bridge are more than six hundred billion to one. But if enough people play long enough, there will be a great many such hands. Given large numbers, and time to burn, the highly improbable happens frequently.

The star shrinks until its central temperature soars to about 10,000,000 degrees Fahrenheit. At that level it stops contracting and enters its period of equilibrium, of slow and steady living. At that level, too, atomic particles move faster than ever. An appreciable proportion of them pair off with one another, merging like two raindrops which meet as they slide down a windowpane. The pairing off of protons or hydrogen nuclei is a first and crucial step in the building of elements. Double-weight particles react more readily. They join with another proton to form triple-weight particles, which in turn are involved in other reactions. At ten million degrees the final product is the quadruple-weight nucleus of helium, the simplest element after hydrogen.

The steady burning of hydrogen fuel yields helium "ashes," and enormous quantities of energy. Every second in our medium-weight star, half a billion tons of hydrogen nuclei undergo fusion and join to form helium nuclei. Every second the star loses several million tons of its mass, releasing energy in the form of radiations. Similar reactions on a much smaller scale take place during the explosion of hydrogen bombs. Scientists, astronomers among them, are working to tame the bomb reactions, to achieve controlled fusion in nuclear furnaces. If they succeed, we will have an almost unlimited supply of energy when our coal and petroleum and uranium are exhausted. We will be using one of nature's most

63

basic processes. The transmutation of hydrogen to helium is the chief source of energy that keeps the stars shining.

We follow the continuing process in one star. As more and more protons combine, helium nuclei accumulate in the core. At first these particles are inert. They have double positive charges, repel each other doubly, and put up a double resistance to further fusion. But it is a losing struggle. Gravitation takes over again, the core of the star contracts, and the gases there become increasingly hot. Then the rising temperature forces the star to expand, which relieves the pressure at the core and cools things down somewhat. The star is becoming less stable, as it proceeds toward the red-giant stage. At temperatures of two hundred million degrees or so, energy levels are high enough to win over the double resistance to synthesis. The next step in the synthesis of elements is under way.

What happens is another most unlikely event, another one of the improbabilities which keep happening and which represent the source of all creation. Without them there would be no novelty and no evolution in the universe. Two helium nuclei come together and remain together for an infinitesimal instant—specifically, for about one-billionth of a billionth of a second. Yet this fleeting "pause" is an interval among atoms, an interval during which important things can take place. Within that period a third helium nucleus smashes into the loosely coupled pair. The three-way collision produces a "shudder," a ripple in space, a gamma ray or high-energy x-ray. It also produces a relatively complex atomic structure resulting from the union of three helium nuclei, each of which was originally formed out of four hydrogen nuclei or protons. The new nucleus has a mass of twelve atomic units. The element carbon has been synthesized.

A few years ago no evidence existed for this reaction. Indeed, there are good arguments against the possibility of a reaction which depends on the vast coincidence of a three-way collision, and against the significance of the reaction in stars even if it were possible. But here is where nuclear research comes in. Since it is not practical to build carbon from three helium nuclei, investigators recently carried out another experiment. They used an electrostatic accelerator, a large machine which produces high-speed atomic particles by subjecting them to "pushes" in the form of lightning-like electrical discharges. They created a form of carbon which disintegrates into three helium nuclei, and showed that the reverse process could occur in stars. On the astronomical side, it is fairly certain that some extra-bright red giants, the brightest stars in ancient clusters, are burning helium in their cores. The spectroscope reveals rich supplies of carbon, presumably built out of helium nuclei, in the atmospheres of other red giants.

Generally speaking, these and other possible ways of going from hydrogen to carbon are well established. We can create and observe the processes or related processes in the laboratory. No basically different process is required to go somewhat further in a "pyramiding" series of reactions which builds more and more elaborate nuclei—and then uses these same new nuclei to form even more complex nuclei. The chain may go from carbon-12 to oxygen-16 to neon-20 by the successive capture of helium-4 nuclei. At this stage the arithmetic of element-building is fairly straightforward, but the creation of heavier elements becomes increasingly difficult.

By the time our star produces neon-20 it has probably used up most of the available helium in its core. Then the heat is really on. The core contracts again, temperatures soar rapidly, and the outer envelope expands still more. If the star manages to stay in one piece under such conditions, it becomes an even bigger red giant. Temperatures of two to six billion degrees may give rise to a new series of atomic species, each weighing four units more than its predecessor: magnesium-24, silicon-28, sulfur-32, and so on. A further rise of three or four billion degrees may be enough to weld particles together and reach elements with weights around 56 (iron, cobalt, nickel).

This is definitely the end of the line for our primeval star. Starting with hydrogen, it can go no further. In fact, going as far as it has gone represents quite a feat. The next step is probably a supernova, an explosion which blows masses of material outward in all directions. Other primeval stars may have exploded before becoming so hot; still others ejected material less violently during their careers. Interstellar space now includes an assortment of elements which may affect the composition and history of new stars. These stars build atomic structures far more elaborate than pioneer stars could.

New possibilities for synthesis occur in second-generation stars which condense out of hydrogen containing dashes of carbon, oxygen, neon, iron, and other elements. At first hydrogen is converted into helium, as in first-generation stars although by a different process. When the available hydrogen at the core is used up and the star is a helium-burning red giant, it also contains special forms or isotopes of carbon, oxygen and neon. These isotopes react with helium nuclei— and yield supplies of extremely important particles, neutrons. Neutrons, as the name implies, are electrically neutral. So, not being repelled by positively charged atomic nuclei, they enter into collisions with relative ease and produce a variety of transmutations, slowly, over periods of thousands to millions of years.

Colliding neutrons help create nuclei of increasing atomic weight. The list starts with the iron group and extends all the way to lead-207 and bismuth-209. This litter of heavier particles includes technetium, whose detection holds such an important place in the development of theories of element-building. It also includes elements of more commercial significance. If present-day views are correct, all the gold and silver and platinum of our earth were originally created inside second-generation red giants. These and other elements were ejected from these stars and used later to make the sun and planets.

Notice when this phase of creation stops. The last elements to be produced weigh somewhat more than two hundred units on the atomic scale, which means that they contain somewhat more than two hundred closely packed protons and neutrons. These complex bodies manage to form an enduring system, to stick together. But they exist close to the weight limit for stable atoms. Most heavier elements are erratic, and tend to change back into lighter elements by ejecting particles from their nuclei. In other words, they are radioactive elements which decay spontaneously.

Radioactive elements must be created by catastrophe. Many neutrons must merge with lighter nuclei, and merge all at once, before the processes of decay go too far. Only supernovae can provide the enormous energies required for such syntheses. So we have second-generation explosions, red giants first collapsing in a single second or so and then bursting and ending as dwarfs. They give birth to the heaviest elements in their dying throes. At temperatures approaching twenty billion degrees such a supernova becomes a star shell, breaking into fragments with the force of trillions of megaton hydrogen bombs. Nuclei may capture many neutrons within seconds or minutes in the rushing climax to creation—yielding radium, uranium and other heavy radioactive elements.

Man has created such elements on earth. Late in 1952 a hydrogen bomb exploded at Bikini Atoll, and a rare reaction took place among the resulting atomic fragments. Uranium atoms and neutrons joined instantaneously in the blinding flash of the explosion. The union produced, among other things, an artificial extra-heavy element: californium-254. Furthermore, there is a hint that the same reaction occurs in supernovae. A supernova may flare up until it is nearly as bright as an entire galaxy of stars. Some time after the outburst it goes into a period of steady decline, fading at a regular rate. In certain supernovae the brightness decreases by about half every 55 days. But 55 days is also the half-life of radioactive californium, and it may be that the dying out of such supernovae is related to the decay of the element in expelled high-velocity gases.

These are only a few aspects of current thinking about the creation of the elements. The full story has not been told. It is highly technical, and much of it is tentative. But as far as broad outlines are concerned, our theories seem to be on the right track. We know that the oldest stars contain relatively low proportions of elements heavier than hydrogen and helium. This is what we would expect if they had formed early in the history of the Milky Way, when element-building had been going on only a short while. We also know that very young stars, born out of a far more varied interstellar mixture, are more than ten times richer than ancient stars in the heavier elements.

Also, recent nuclear studies in astronomy tend to confirm the important notion that a great many stars were formed swiftly in the beginning. The sun is still in its hydrogen-burning stage and has certainly never synthesized any element heavier than helium. Yet it contains all the elements known on earth, including such heavyweights as uranium. In other words, the sun is something of a mongrel and must be made up of materials formed in many previous stars, one of which was perhaps a supernova. Elements weighing up to 56 units or so, the iron group, arose in primeval red giants which presumably burst in due course. Heavier elements in the sun could only have been produced by neutron reactions in stars which at birth included some debris from ancestral giants. The heaviest radioactive elements came into being as these second-generation stars died with supernova bangs. So according to nuclear theory, the sun is a third-generation star.

If the theory is correct, the early days of our galaxy were

rather cataclysmic. The sun is about five to six billion years old, and there are many stars like it. The Milky Way itself is not a great deal older. It probably began jelling into stars not much more than seven billion years ago. But think what that implies for the two billion or so years between the birth of the first stars and the birth of stars roughly contemporary with the sun. The galaxy was living a wild life—and time was very short.

During that period element-building must have proceeded at a breakneck pace. All elements above hydrogen must have been created in sufficient quantities to account for the composition of legions of later stars. And the ingredients had to be mixed thoroughly in interstellar space. To do the mixing on a large scale required flares and outbursts and other violent activity, including two generations of supernovae. If all this happened, there must have been a high proportion of bright-blue, fast-living hell-raisers among the primeval stars of the Milky Way. Star-making then was something quite different from what it is now.

A fuller understanding of these processes may alter certain notions about the beginnings of the universe. All stars in the earliest stages of element-building produce enormous quantities of another atomic particle, the neutrino. Neutrinos, like neutrons, have no electrical charge. They have no mass either, and may be regarded as bullets of pure energy. Moving at the speed of light, they react with nothing and no atom can capture them. So they travel away from the stars, and on and on beyond the limits of the observable universe.

Streams of neutrino-energy are flowing out of the stars in all directions and out of the colonies of stars called galaxies. Could these streams have anything to do with the expansion of the universe? Perhaps galaxies were not born after the bursting of the cosmic egg. Things may have happened the other way around. Perhaps the expansion is a secondary rather than a primary event, which somehow began after helium was first formed in a hydrogen universe. These speculations suggest that we may yet discover a basic relationship between the expanding universe and the creation of elements.

Our theories are certain to change considerably during the years ahead. But there is no doubt about one thing. The very large and the very small, the visible and the invisible, are closely connected in the physical universe. Reactions among atoms which may occur in a vanishingly small fraction of a second provide the energy for giant stars billions of years old. Stellar evolution and element-building are not two separate processes, but part of the same universal shaping of matter. The production of atoms with more and more complex structures takes place along with and because of the unfolding of patterns among the stars.

So little yields so much. Space is practically a vacuum and matter is barely a contamination of the vacuum, a wisp of smoke in an infinite sky. And of that wisp only the faintest trace consists of the stuff that goes chiefly into the making of planets and satellites and all the rest that is to come. On the average, out of every 10,000 atoms in the universe, 9300 are hydrogen and 699 are helium atoms. The lone remaining atom represents one of the other elements. It may be carbon or oxygen or neon or silicon, a major constituent of rocks.

But evolution from here on involves extremely rare elements to an increasing extent. Galaxies, stars, elements. The odds against existence continue to mount, more and more unlikely things continue to appear and persist. Evolving matter continues to generate more and more improbable patterns.

One Star and
One Planet
5

NOW we come closer to home, to a theory about how the solar system came into being. Like all theories, this one involves a measure of imagination. It is a blend of fact and speculation, heavier on the speculative side than we might wish, but still more sophisticated by a comfortable margin than notions which prevailed not long ago.

Closer to home, and another beginning in our series of beginnings. More than five billion years ago, some time after the heyday of star-making, a mass of gaseous stuff drifts inside a spiral arm of the Milky Way. The cloud, like many others before and since, starts evolving and passing through the customary stages of a process already old. It starts to contract and its thickening core will become a star—our sun. The shaping of the star, of course, is the major development under way at this particular time and place. It requires the great bulk of the cloud stuff and it will produce the largest structure.

But we are not concerned primarily with the main attraction, with what is happening in the thick of things. We are concerned with fringe events, suburban processes quite incidental to the business of building another star. The cloud contracts from its original diameter of ten thousand billion miles or so to a core about ten million times smaller, a considerable reduction. It is as if an object the size of the moon shrank to match-head proportions. The core now contains more than ninety percent of the matter that made up the cloud. It has not finished shrinking. It spins, a dark region inside thinner gases, like a marble in a puff of smoke.

The smoke represents all that remains of the cloud, the excess fraction that did not have to be used for the shaping of the sun. It is waste material, a kind of stellar garbage which would not have to be cast aside if star-making were one hundred percent efficient. Leftover material like sawdust or the chips on the floor after a piece of sculpture is completed—except that it will not be discarded. In an afterthought, a cleaning-up operation, the scraps will be put to use. The little nebula will become a system of satellites, and satellites of satellites.

There is a struggle at first. The core that is shrinking at the center, the embryonic and still-unshining sun, exerts a gravitational pull on the gases of the nebula. The pull discourages the formation of further bodies, stirring up the gases and tending to disperse them. Other forces have an opposite effect. They tend not only to bring matter together, but also to bring it together in a number of individual extra-dense clumps. The nebula spins along with the core, faster and faster. It flattens so that its gases are compressed into a narrower and narrower wafer-shaped zone. That increases the density of the nebula as a whole.

Meanwhile the density increases locally within the cramped quarters. Vortices form, like the small sucking whirlpools of water flowing down drains. The vortices give rise to a group of clumps, which have internal gravitational forces. And at one point these centers of high density and attraction within the nebula achieve identities of their own. Self-gravitation takes over, becomes more powerful than the dispersing effects of tides from the solar core. Instead of a diffuse nebula we have a string of vaguely globular forms, a soft spray of gas droplets.

One of the smallest droplets, the third-nearest the core, will become the earth after a sequence of appropriate changes. A blob of gas only beginning to condense, still about fourteen million miles in diameter or more than seventeen hundred times the present diameter of the earth. And now a process picks up speed, a process that had already started in the original nebula. So far our story has been chiefly of misty materials, near-vacuums and clouds and hazes. Now we begin dealing with solids and liquids as well. Gradually more substantial stuff appears among oceans of vapor. Such changes may take place if atoms are crowded together in sufficiently cool environments.

Deep-freeze. This portion of space is more than sufficiently cool, about minus-350 degrees Fahrenheit. Matter may change from gas to liquid to solid. Crystals are about to come, conditions are ready for chain reactions once condensation proceeds far enough. The formation of a single crystal in one zone may set things off. It is a model for copying, a nucleus about which similar crystals form. Particles stick fast to its surfaces and freeze into patterns and become nuclei for further freezings. The seeding process speeds itself and all at once there are flurries of snowflakes and ice crystals, needle-shaped fragments like microscopic icicles.

A new variety of pattern. Not so much curved things such as globes and spirals, but straight-lined and edged and faceted things, frigid jewels. Geometric designs, hexagons and prisms and pyramids and cubes, resembling forms shaped in frost on a windowpane during a winter night. There are similar crystals in comets and in clouds of interstellar dust which obscure many stars of today's Milky Way.

Crystals, another step in the evolution of matter. Vast populations of atoms come together, but not in hordes or mobs. Orderly and disciplined congregations, like soldiers standing at attention, rigid and eyes front. An army of regimented atoms, a crystal. Take a barely visible crystal, a cube no bigger than a grain of sand. It is a lattice structure of particles arranged in fixed positions in space. Each edge of the cube may consist of 400,000 lined-up atoms. Crystals have some remarkable properties. They are inanimate but subtle. They hint at the nature of things to come, for they can grow and reproduce themselves.

During the deep-freeze, crystals grow in the gases, falling together and joining. Matter merging into solid particles, so-called planetesimals. This is another self-accelerating process. Once a group of particles clots together, it becomes more massive and attracts more particles and grows even more rapidly. Under prevailing conditions it takes a year or two to grow a particle about the size of the tip of your little finger, tens of thousands of years to grow a body half a mile in diameter. So the crystals that will make a world continue to accumulate and fall together, spiraling in toward larger masses like bees into a hive. And the masses meet and fuse. Successive condensations, resembling in a way the building of heavier and heavier atomic nuclei during the creation of elements. There is breakdown as well as fusion. Masses collide and pulverize one another. But certain masses grow and are not shattered.

The snowballing takes a long time. About a hundred million years pass, and even then it seems to be just starting. Only about two-tenths of a percent of the gas droplets have condensed into solid stuff near the center. At this early stage the material consists of relatively high proportions of elements heavier than hydrogen and helium—including the first

74

elements to condense, such as iron and nickel and other metals, and chemically active elements like oxygen, which combine with other elements in firm molecular bonds. (Similar activities are taking place in more remote zones, inside other gas droplets, protoplanets which will become Mars and Jupiter and Saturn and the rest of the solar system.)

Presumably the rest of the gases will condense later. There is plenty of raw material, enough to make many, many bodies as heavy as the earth. If it could all condense into one planet, the earth would be a Leviathan more massive than all the other planets put together. At present the bulk of the original droplet is a great halo or atmosphere which surrounds two solid kernels. The kernels will merge into a single body, assuming that things proceed as expected.

But things do not always go according to expectations. If they did, there would be no surprises and no novelty—and the time is getting ripe for novelty. The sun is maturing. A new development is about to begin. The signal of the beginning is a light, faint at first but gradually brightening. The solar system has been dark for a long, long time, a black and cold place among the shining ranks of established stars. Now it is the newcomer's turn.

A glow appears at the center of the solar system, inside the gaseous globe of the sun. The glow marks a natural and familiar stage of stellar evolution. The sun has been shrinking and the material at the interior has been growing hotter and hotter. The first rays of sunlight are dim and red. But they become more intense and yellower as the temperature rises toward the equilibrium level where the sun stops contracting and hydrogen fuel burns steadily.

Another light comes on in the Milky Way. The sun is shining and its radiations heat near-by gases, which once existed at subzero temperatures, to perhaps as much as 200,000 degrees Fahrenheit. The seething gases expand. Their atoms accelerate until they attain speeds of some 18,000 miles a minute. A shell of outward-bound particles racing through space, a barrage of projectiles. First of all, the atoms collide with and disperse the tenuous remnants of the original nebula, the material that has never been captured by protoplanets, sweeping clean the space between the primeval condensations of the solar system.

Then continuing streams of particles go to work on the atmospheres which still cling stubbornly to the protoplanets. The regions nearest the sun feel the force of the blasting barrage first. In the region where a bare earth will be, most of the atmosphere is blown off in an enormous gale toward the outer parts of the solar system and toward interstellar space. The entire sweeping away lasts several hundred million years at least. It accelerates as the sun brightens and tapers off when more than ninety percent of the gases have been dispersed. Wheat from chaff, gas from solid, a sorting-out process on a grand scale. All that remains is a number of bodies too cool to produce their own light. They shine by proxy, by the sun's reflected light.

The illumination of the sun has stopped condensation dead in its tracks. A process has ceased with the dissipation of gases that might have become crystals, leaving solid objects naked of atmospheres. Perhaps some of the objects would have been merged with one another to form still larger bodies, but that possibility has also been eliminated. For example, here in the region where in the future a more complex kind of condensation will appear—man—the two kernels of matter might have merged. Instead we see a satellite of the sun, the primeval planet earth. And the satellite of a satellite, the earth's lone companion, the moon.

Similar processes are believed to have given rise to the eight other planets. Their thirty-odd moons condensed one by one out of flattened subnebulae, gas discs surrounding the planets somewhat as the original nebula surrounded the sun. The rings of Saturn represent material that never condensed into moons. Other protoplanets formed, at least two and probably more. But the traffic was apparently too heavy. They collided in the remote past and broke into bits and the bits recollided, so that now we have thousands of asteroids or minor planets, and swarms of meteors. The comets were made out of material at the outer fringes of the original nebula. This is the genesis of the solar system according to one theory, one effort to piece together as many observed facts as possible.

We have come through a long series of steps on our way to solidity. One great original cloud which broke into galaxies, subclouds separating out of the galaxies to form stars, and still smaller fragments separating out of the subcloud that forms the sun. Then finally the fragments condense into planets and moons. Certain observations and experiments suggest how all this may have happened. But much of it is theory, and that is especially true of the shaping of the solar system. There is still a wide gap between astronomy and geology, a gap which makes it difficult to explain the origin of the earth on the basis of events known to take place among the stars.

So the theory we have outlined is by no means accepted in all its details. But it does one thing that any succeeding theory will have to do. It takes account of the fact that, on the face of it, the chemical composition of the earth is exceedingly peculiar. The original cloud, the forming galaxies, and the earliest stars probably consisted of hydrogen and little else. Hydrogen and helium make up almost all the substance of the sun and other later stars. Even the protoplanets were chiefly hydrogen and helium at one stage of their development. But this is not the case for some of the sun's satellites, including the earth.

The primeval earth has only traces of the two most abundant elements in the universe. Certain other elements, such as argon and neon, are millions or billions of times rarer on earth than they are in the sun and the stars. What is just as significant, the earth contains abnormally large concentrations of metals and silicon and oxides, compounds of oxygen with other elements—as well as relatively abundant supplies of radioactive substances.

The oxides, by the way, include some lightweight compounds which do not condense readily and tend to remain in the gaseous state. They are trapped or built into more complex crystal material. Water combines with silicon compounds and is also bound tight in the primeval earth. But if it had escaped as completely as neon, for example, the earth would be a Sahara. On the average the "oceans" would be somewhat less than a tenth of an inch deep.

Generally speaking, the earth is made up chiefly of substances which make up less than half of one percent of the universe as a whole.

These are some of the facts which we seek to explain in terms of natural phenomena. Our theories represent the most powerful techniques yet developed for working toward such explanations. A successful theory is a strange creation. Assume that it accounts for all currently known facts and, in that sense, is true. It will remain true for a time only, until new facts are found which do not fit into our ideas about the nature of things. And the new facts are always found. Then the theory is no longer strictly true (although it may continue to be fruitful). In other words, the most one can expect from a theory is that it be true for a while. Sooner or later it is sure to be proved false for all time. In science, being right is a temporary thing, but you can be wrong forever.

Of what use are theories then? They are feelers of a sort, antennae of the mind which reach out a bit beyond the borders of what we know now and grope a little way into the unknown. They extend possibilities, suggest new experiments, predict what we may yet discover. And, of course, they lead to their own disproof. Many theories about the origin of the earth and the solar system have been discarded in the light of new research. Current theories are designed to include recent findings relevant to the chemistry of the primeval earth, and to account for subsequent processes which shaped and are still shaping the earth today.

The primeval earth is hardly an attractive place. Nearly two hundred million square miles of surface area and not an acre worth living on, even if it could support life. An over-sized chunk of metal and stone all squeezed together in a mineral jumble resembling a mammoth meteorite. There is a steady downpour of solid stuff too heavy to have been blown away when the sun began shining—microscopic and barely visible particles, bodies of many sizes, pulled by the force of gravity. They strike the surface hard and fast, eventually fusing with and becoming part of the earth. A falling of crystalline hailstones on a globe of jagged rock. Everywhere the same barren landscape.

It will take a chemical revolution to change all this, to put the spark of life into this dead place. To make a planet into a world. The earth, a composite built up of countless planetesimals stuck together, is monotonous inside as well as outside. Its different substances are so thoroughly mixed with one another, its material is so evenly distributed, that few distinguishing features exist. Creating variety requires a rough separation and division of different compounds, a complete reshuffling of terrestrial chemicals. Until that happens there will be no oceans and mountains and valleys and rivers.

The reshuffling comes with changes of climate inside the earth. First, a long hot summer. The impacts of falling bodies produce heat, particularly in regions near the surface. Also, the earth is still shrinking, compressing itself. Gravitational forces squeeze materials at the center, causing a steady rise of temperature. And radioactivity is at its height. Larger quantities of undecayed radioactive elements exist at this stage of the earth's history than will ever exist again, and the heat generated by exploding atoms is locked up beneath the surface. Such effects produce temperatures of 3000 to 4000 degrees Fahrenheit or more—and things begin to shift and simmer.

Vast portions of the earth turn into slushy molten masses, melted rock, primeval lava. According to one theory, these masses may be regarded as metallic ores particularly rich in iron. The interior of the earth has become a sealed crucible in which a long series of chemical reactions is about to take place, one of the earliest being the extraction of iron. Molten iron sinks down into the depths, separating from the rest of the "ores." Many millions of years pass and the metals accumulate in a deep pool, forming a core at the center of the earth which consists mostly of liquid iron.

Imagine a mining effort organized to tap this abundant supply. There are about forty billion cubic miles of metal, if we could get at the core. Gold, platinum and other precious materials as well as iron. Enough gold, for example, to enclose the earth in a great spherical shell about a yard thick. But engineers would have to dig a shaft extending some eighteen hundred miles beneath the surface, more than a third of the way to the center, to reach the core's outer boundary. (Of course, the earth might be destroyed long before they reached that level, as unleashed pressures of millions of pounds per square inch began producing earthquakes and other upheavals!)

The formation of the core is one phase in the early chemistry of the earth's interior. A lighter and partly molten mix is left floating on top of the thick, heavy core, a layer resting on top of a liquid, resembling the slag which floats on molten iron in a blast furnace. Blast-furnace slag represents what remains from the original ore, and the earth's floating stuff is also leftover material. This residue, this flowing scum, consists chiefly of iron bound to silicon, magnesium and that part of the original iron which does not separate out into the core. Mixed in with the major ingredients are all the other sub-

80

stances of the earth—including rare metals, water, carbon, sulfur, phosphorous, and radioactive elements to keep things warm.

This slag measures eighteen hundred miles deep. It is an extremely complex solution of matter in solid, liquid and gaseous states. It is cooling near the exposed surface, where heat escapes into space, cooling from the top down. And reactions proceed accordingly, from the top down. The first material to take shape within the solution is probably a mineral named olivine because of its olive-green color. Its crystals contain atoms of silicon, iron, magnesium and oxygen in typical lattice patterns—elements formed long ago in vanished stars. The mineral hardens and sinks through the melt, settles at the bottom, and begins to form a deep solid shell around the core of the earth.

Chemical laws determine a broad sequence of subsequent crystallizations. Cooling proceeds and temperatures dip toward the "freezing" or solidifying points for other types of minerals. After olivine comes another material containing the same elements as olivine but arranged in different crystal designs. Later deep-red transparent crystals of garnet appear, and perhaps some diamond. And still later more and more different minerals and crystals, for the variety of the good earth becomes richer and richer toward the surface. All the beautiful and not-so-beautiful rocks listed and classified in technical handbooks—and christened with an even richer variety of strange names, which mean everything to mineralogists and nothing to the rest of us. Gems in the making, crystals with a spectrum of colors wider than rainbows.

Patterns out of the slag. The successive phases are not clean-cut and distinct, as they may be when we observe crystallizations out of rock melted in the laboratory. The crystals of each batch of sinking material are mixed and intermeshed with some crystals from preceding batches. But there seems to be little doubt about the general tendency. The earth is building itself into a system of shells upon shells. And all the time the slag on top becomes thinner and thinner, as crystal masses form and fall away into the depths and deplete its substance. At last a bare film of slag remains near the outer surface of the planet. This will become the earth's crust, a two-shell affair with an average depth of about twenty miles.

The earth is still a gloomy place, with a recently formed outer layer of dark rock. But it continues to cool, and many things can happen when temperatures fall. Atoms rearrange themselves, crystals become distorted and change their structure. Tremendous stresses and strains build up and must be relieved in some way. Glass plunged into hot water may shatter. Even thick steel plates cooled or "quenched" too rapidly bend and twist and crack. Fortunately, the earth was never quenched. Rock cools slowly. A few million years ago a huge block of granite was forced up through the surface of the earth in a region which is now Yellowstone Park. The granite has been cooling ever since, but its temperature is still high enough to produce geysers and hot springs.

Slow, deep cooling in the primeval earth is still enough to upset the balance of things locally—rumblings deep underground and uneasy movements at the surface. Events on the earth today give only a mild hint of what must have been happening then. The floor of a smoldering crater is brittle and porous, and there are holes around with thick bubbling fluids inside and smoke coming out. Walking across the floor, picking your way through the holes, you feel that any minute you may fall through, and you step softly. Imagine great areas on the earth's surface, hundreds of square miles, in a similar state—smoldering in the imminence of breakthroughs and upheavals to come.

Cooling ultimately produces fractures, canyon-wide cracks moving like horizontal lightning, ripping open the belly of earth. And hot materials from the depths are squeezed out of the openings. Again, no experience to draw upon, only the

CRYSTALS

STRUCTURE OF GENETIC MATERIAL

Thread of material magnified under electron microscope.

What higher magnification would show—coils within coils

Still higher magnification—the DNA molecule

birth of a few small volcanoes. Late one afternoon in February 1943 a Mexican farmer discovered something near a cave on his land, something which had not been there the day before. He saw a long split in the earth and suddenly "felt a thunder" beneath his feet. The ground heaved, and smoke and ashes came out of the crack. He heard hissing, smelled sulfur, and prayed to a saint: "You brought me into this world—now save me from the dangers in which I am about to die." Paricutin reached a height of only fifteen hundred feet and then stopped growing.

Imagine upheavals sufficient to produce chains of super-Paricutins, the first chains of volcanic mountains. The earth is fidgeting, shifting, adjusting the weights of hot and cool masses, working toward a peaceful equilibrium that has not yet been attained. The safety valves are opening. Fountains of spark and ash and lava burst out of the cracks, and the lava piles up. Later great "shields" form, massive blocks of granite—nuclei that grow like gargantuan crystals and perhaps meet and fuse. Lands of granite floating like rafts on heavier rock underneath. These nuclei are the beginnings of continents. A world is taking shape.

Other events run concurrent with the building of mountains and continents. An atmosphere will make its appearance, but at this stage it is still mostly buried, sealed inside the earth. Its raw materials include some of the light, volatile substances that were locked in crystals or built into heavy molecules during earlier times, when things were condensing out of the solar nebula. Now they are being released from volcanoes, along with ash and lava, and from the mouths of geysers and hot springs. The earth, having lost one atmosphere, is in the process of providing itself with another, a thick and humid one.

The oceans also come from the interior, at least partly by a roundabout route. Some years ago a geologist estimated the total flow of water from all present-day hot springs, those active undersea as well as those on land, and arrived at a conservative figure of more than thirty million gallons per minute. The springs of the primeval earth flow more abundantly, not to mention the volcanoes which spout water vapor, among other things. The vapor enters the hothouse atmosphere. There are dense clouds, and thunders and lightnings —and rain, millions of years of extra-heavy rain. Waters rush unretarded down slopes of bare rock, and the basins of earth begin filling. The oceans are falling from the skies.

Mountains, continents, atmosphere, oceans—the early days of the earth, the days which lie beyond nostalgia and about which we know least. There are many theories and disagreements and many guesses, shrewd and otherwise. Every theory considerably oversimplifies the course of events, because so much remains to be learned. Some investigators are candid about such things, and one of them, an outstanding American geochemist, has this to say: "We need to do so much more basic research, detailed studies of the physics and chemistry of the earth. Right now we have only crude pictures at best. As a matter of fact most of our theories about the formation of the earth are fairy tales, toothpick castles that won't hold up."

Not that we should belittle our fairy tales and the toothpick castles. They often represent the work of constructive investigators who know that a theory which stimulates new observations and experiments is far better than no theory at all. It is not to the point that critics will almost certainly rip the theory to ribbons. (In science, as in other fields, the people who dare receive the main share of the scorn as well as the praise.) The main thing is that it lead somewhere. A specialist so afraid of losing prestige that he never sticks his neck out is not likely to make significant contributions to the advancement of science.

The more we learn about the restless youth of the solar system, the better we understand even wider problems. For the shaping of the earth marks an important phase in the evolution of matter as we know it—an ending of a sort, and a fresh beginning. A phase in the ordering of substance, of an exceedingly scarce impurity which contaminates what would otherwise be sheer nothingness. The question of the origin of the contaminant, the source of the substance which pollutes space, is at present unanswerable. We cannot offer explanations for this beginning, if there ever was such a beginning, but we accept it because it exists.

We also accept gravitation, or whatever you call the clotting tendency of matter. Without it there would be thinning clouds, universal scattering and nothing else. The nuclei of atoms repel one another so powerfully that temperatures in the millions of degrees are needed to bring them within mutual hailing distance. But the forces of repulsion are not powerful enough. If isolation could ever work it would certainly be at the atomic level and in the universe, where there is so much room and so little substance.

The fact that matter actually congregates among such vastnesses is almost beyond belief. It is somewhat like two people with the whole earth to themselves fighting for the best seat in a deserted theater. Complete isolation seems far more plausible. Gravitation spoils all that, continually counteracting utter dispersion, utter lack of order. Atoms become clannish almost despite themselves, and the problem of the individual against the organization exists among them in a purely physical form.

So, starting with substance and gravitation, things work themselves out according to laws which we understand in part. Progressive thickening from a cloud of hydrogen gas to a family of clouds that will form galaxies, and then to stars where all the elements are built from hydrogen. Atoms brought closer and closer to one another, so close that some of them may interact. Progressive thickening to solid stuff and crystals, the ultimate in one class of patterns—inanimate patterns. There are two other classes of patterns as far as we know, living patterns and human or cultural patterns. They have become possible because of the condensations of matter. But they are more than condensations; they involve new complexities of organization, bursts of variety.

These patterns will take their places in our story. Now—that is, roughly three to four billion years ago—we have only a recent satellite in a universe of galaxies. It is a crystal place, a rocky globe composed chiefly of elements that have lived through eventful times. The substance of the earth was born in the hot and congested interiors of stars which have disappeared or exist no more as they once were. It has been fused and forged in floating furnaces that burst apart and scattered long ago, created in supernovae and incandescent geysers spurting out of dying burned-out suns.

In some ways the substance of the earth resembles ashes, all that is left of fires that have stopped burning. But perhaps the analogy should not be pushed too far, and it is so easy to mistake beginnings for endings. The earth is young and has a great deal of evolving to do. Soon the "ashes" will ferment, if they have not already started fermenting. Everything is ready. The ingredients have been prepared and mixed, and the sun will keep them simmering. Nature is cooking up something new, the most improbable improbability yet. A new variety of pattern, life, is about to join the population of crystals in this mineral world.

LIFE

Molecules That Evolve

6

THE stream of organization continues. Pattern upon pattern, beginning after beginning in the teeth of death and decay. Novelty springing up where things seem to have come to an end. Evolution leaping the "impossible" gap from inanimate stuff to cells and beyond. Has it happened here on earth only or in many other places? Is life rare, or does life spread everywhere in a universal epidemic? It makes a difference.

It is possible that we are alone in the universe. Life and mind may be confined to the earth. If so, we go it alone and we go in a kind of glory. We are unique, and from one standpoint all the universe and all the stars revolve about us. Ours is the drama of the lone wolf, the defiant outcast, the hero, the half-god. There is one living world, one highest species, one and only one Christ or Mohammed or Buddha. But we live with a terrible burden in the widest of all imaginable lonelinesses, and when we go, everything is gone everywhere.

The more unique we are, the deeper the possibility of despair. The cosmos is an infinite moor with one house on it.

If life is common and worlds grow in the warmth of other suns, we become less in one sense and more in another. We are less unique, and our myths and aspirations are less special. Other planets have their validities, their renaissances and resurrections and revelations. But we are not so alone. Our burden is lighter, for we have company in space and our peers may be found everywhere. Life is not something aside from the point, something sitting off on the sidelines. We are sharers, players not spectators. In this universe we are part of the main hubbub of things. This moor has many houses, and there may yet be pathways among them.

Science has something to say about such alternatives and the philosophies that go with them. Not long ago there was support for the notion that our solar system is the result of an extremely rare event. Once upon a time, according to the theory, another star flew like a missile through space and headed toward the sun. It failed to make a direct hit, but came so close that its gravitational attraction pulled a long streamer or filament of gas away from the sun—and the planets condensed out of the material after the star had passed.

Such an explanation implies that life is rare indeed. In the first place, the odds against the accident of a near-collision are enormous and therefore the formation of planets is most unlikely. Furthermore, the odds against the appearance of living matter are even greater because not all planets provide the right conditions. So the "sideswipe" theory, like all theories involving suddenness and catastrophe, argues for a sort of special creation. Presumably the circumstances which produced protoplasm might have come to pass once and only once.

But astronomers have had to discard this theory. It simply does not work. For example, we know now that matter pulled from the sun in such a way would not condense to solid stuff, but would explode and disperse itself. Modern theories have entirely different implications. As far as we know, all stars form from clouds of gas, and if planets form at the same time out of the same gases, they must be quite common. In fact, nowadays some investigators believe that practically every star has planets and that stars without planets are freaks. This means that the Milky Way contains about a hundred billion solar systems. Assuming that only one out of a thousand such systems, say, contains living matter, there are a hundred million inhabited planets in our galaxy alone— and the known universe contains at least five hundred million other galaxies.

We still do not have proof positive that inhabited planets, or even uninhabited planets for that matter, revolve about other stars. But everything we know suggests that planet-making is a common thing, and an investigator who believed otherwise would have to seek special evidence to the contrary. Such evidence does not exist now. Life may be rarer than planets, but we have no reason to think that it is particularly unique, either. So our universe probably houses a large number of living worlds and a large number of worlds where life has not yet arrived but is imminent.

Evolution under way in many places, differing in different solar systems perhaps, but always working by the inherent logic of matter. In all cases a building-up of substance, an increase in complexity which has been going on for ten billion years. The coming of chemical elements—beginning with nuclei of hydrogen, the simplest and lightest element, and proceeding step after step in burning star cores to the synthesis of the more and more elaborate nuclei of heavier elements. The coming of life, wherever it occurs—beginning with the elements and simple combinations of elements, and going by easy stages to intricate materials which reproduce and breed and evolve. What is about to happen on earth may represent a model of fundamental processes that have taken place and are taking place throughout the universe.

We start with desolation. Imagine life vanishing from the earth as you watch. You sit near the edge of the sea looking into a pool. A school of silver-green fish darts in formation in and out of tousled seaweed. A crab scrambles sideways out of a crevice, pink shell outlined sharp against white sand, routed by some larger creature inside.

Suddenly the pool goes dark and blurs, ruffled for an instant as if a huge ripple had rushed over the surface. But there is no wind. It is a moment of terrible magic. The blur passes. The pool is clear again and you see that it has been stripped bare. Everything alive has disappeared—the fish, the seaweed, the crab, everything and all the colors of life, gone. You look up from the pool at an ocean gray and dull as a dead eye in a nightmare. You are alone among rocks. Rocks close at hand, steaming places among rocks inland, land to the horizon without houses or trees or grass, mountains of rock on the horizon like pyramid tombs in the desert. This is the earth in its early days.

We start on an infant and barren world, a world covered with a thick, gray, wrinkled elephant skin of rock. There are seas and pools by the seas, but they are dead pools and the seas are dead. There is motion, but it is inanimate motion. The swell of warm waters, the rising of sulfurous steams, the shifting of rocks and great rifts in the ground and lava welling out of the rifts. A wasteland, another unlikely place for beginnings.

Yet wastelands may be deceptive. Nature may be merely playing possum; and this desolation is desolation with a future. If the earth were truly isolated, if there were no give and take between it and the rest of the universe, it might well remain lifeless for all eternity. But no part of the universe is really alone. Disturb substance in a star or a cloud of interstellar gas, in this galaxy or in another galaxy, and sooner or later matter far away will respond to the disturb-

Molecules That Evolve

ance. Space is like a communications network or a nervous system—all interconnected—or a pool, where the falling away of a leaf or a twig sends ripples to other shores.

Ripples of energy. The nearest star glows and the glow will help produce life. Rhythms and beats in the nuclear furnace at the heart of the sun. Disturbed atoms in the sun oscillate like the strings of a violin. The oscillations produce radiation, waves of energy, the pounding of a submicroscopic surf. Ultraviolet rays stream away from the sun, outward in all directions. Some of the ripples move toward the earth, enter a primeval atmosphere, and wherever they pass matter is ruffled. They leave wakes behind them, little disturbances arising from the original disturbances in the sun.

Atoms in the earth's atmosphere respond to rhythms born in the sun. They resonate, oscillate in phase and take up the beat, somewhat as objects on shelves and tables shudder and vibrate from a loud, piercing musical note. Things are being stirred up again, and not only by the steady flow of solar radiation. Pulses in the earth's atmosphere itself may contribute to the stirring up. Storms move over the earth, dark clouds collide. Electricity flashes and there are more violent disturbances. Lightning as well as ultraviolet rays from the sun set atoms oscillating.

Waves and sparks in the skies. Flurries of atoms in an excited state, reacting with one another more readily than they would under quieter conditions. Patterns generated above the earth, materials synthesized which are new here and now but may have appeared before in other places. Simple organic compounds may have existed among the stars or in the crystal planetesimals that merged to make the earth. Now they are forming at relatively high rates, and the rains come and wash them down into the seas.

Elements built out of clouds in remote suns, star dust of a sort, combine in the waters of the satellite earth. Things are happening invisibly, and they will remain invisible for hundreds of millions of years. Substance adrift, atomic flotsam. Particles dart and swerve and bounce off one another, and sometimes stick together. They form shapes and fragments of shapes, Tinker Toy lattices and crosses and branching structures and unclassified patterns resembling the forms in some modern paintings. Molecules in ring and cage formations, molecules with short side chains jutting out like thorns. Matter moving ceaselessly in solution, a shuffling of atoms.

It is not gravity that holds things together now, but the attraction of electrically charged particles, chemical bonds. The seas become a rich broth of organic stuff which accumulates in all waters—masses of organic matter, billions and billions of tons, a supply house of compounds among which may be found precursors for the parts of reproducing systems. There are abundant quantities of amino acids, structures of ten to twenty atoms, units like snap-together links that may join to form a variety of more complex molecules. There are natural pigments, colored substances, light filters which can absorb radiations from the sun, and substances storing energy in their chemical bonds like atomic pieces of coal.

The ocean is a brew that simmers with many ingredients. Heat comes from the exploding atoms of radioactive materials and from the flow and bubbling of deep molten matter and lava. Ultraviolet rays reach the surface of uneasy waters. Primeval tides and gales and upheavals on shores and undersea keep the mix stirring. Yet the mix and the stirring are not enough by themselves. We need something more, because synthesis is limited in most places.

In most places synthesis can go so far and no further. Many new substances are being shaped, and being destroyed. Energy alone works in the dark, and creates and annihilates pattern blindly. It brings molecules together and tears them apart. Heat, for example, affects reactions unselectively, speeding synthesis and breakdown at the same time. Here a number of amino acids are linked, and the links break almost as soon as they form. Here a new structure forms only to be shattered by the same forces that built it. Heavy molecular traffic moves in both directions, a continual shuttling back and forth, ceaseless weaving and unweaving as if performed by a mad weaver. Things arise and are snuffed out.

But the processes of synthesis, of novelty, win as they have always won. Victory takes place off-stage, in the wings, not where the main action seems to be going on. Once not so long ago planets condensed in a cloud away from the center where the big event was taking place, the creation of a star—and now in a similar fashion matter forms significant new patterns away from the central swirls of things. Victory does not always come in the midst of spectacular displays. It does not come where waters heave green or currents wind into whirlpools or surf pounds itself into foam.

Synthesis is proceeding in places of hush. In rock pools, mud flats and marshes and ponds, where ripples may move in unbroken circles. Substances come together and concentrate in quiet waters, shielded from the most disruptive forces. Scums may float on unruffled surfaces and protect other materials just below from the sun's radiations. The materials precipitate and sink to the bottoms of pools where rays cannot reach, or perhaps they drift into dark waters beneath rock ceilings. Under such conditions, in water stillnesses and the peace of stagnation, many things happen.

Mineral crystals, the most symmetrical patterns of inanimate evolution, may promote the growth of organic patterns. The faces and edges of quartz, mica and other crystals offer footholds for new materials. Molecules moving in solution near the sides or the bottom of a pool make contacts with crystal surfaces and stick there. The structure of the crystal imposes a structure on the particles clinging to it. Amino acids may line up along the edges of prisms and hexagonal sheets and combine as the links of chain molecules, simple proteins or fragments of proteins. Material accumulates in reactive zones, attaining concentrations hundreds or thousands of times greater than those which exist in surrounding waters.

Time passes and pattern begets pattern. Long-chain molecules make fibers and the fibers mat together. Transparent films bend and curl into intricate surfaces. Globules form, little spheroids where substances may react within the shelter of thin elastic walls. The globules are not cells; that development lies ages and ages in the future. They are merely bodies which look something like cells and have not yet learned the trick of enduring or reproducing. But they may persist for surprisingly long periods, like bubbles of foam swept up on a seashore and blown about and leaving little scoops along the sand, where they bounce before bursting. Globules taking shape under water also collapse eventually. But first they drift, temporary centers of chemical activity and new syntheses. Their substance leaks away when they burst. New globules form in other places, however, and pattern-making goes on.

The most actively simmering parts of the primeval soup are like fluid webs, networks of chemical reactions. Different processes may lead to the same end product, and processes yielding different end products share some of the intermediate compounds. Crisscrossing and interlocking sequences of molecular events, mazes of processes going every which way. And along with all this activity, in the midst of the mazes, something else is happening. Many, many processes are under way and gradually some of them begin to dominate the others. For a while at least, certain processes are favored because of the concurrent and related evolution of a remarkable class of substances called catalysts.

Catalysts speed the pace of things. They are soon at work

in the waters of the earth. The building of chemical structures near the bottoms of sluggish pools, for example, involves collisions among moving molecules. But this is a very slow way of getting things done, of forming sugars and starches and proteins. Collisions come infrequently, and the odds are that only one out of billions and billions of collisions will result in a chemical reaction. Catalysts represent one of nature's most effective ways of beating the odds, of "cheating" in what would otherwise be a game of pure chance with no winnings.

Most of the catalysts in the organic broths of the primeval earth are simple compounds or single electrically charged atoms. (More elaborate compounds will come later.) They contain reactive sites, spots where other particles may attach themselves. The attached particles are held in position and stay near enough to one another, long enough, so that they combine to form new compounds. In other words, a catalyst concentrates particles, bringing them close together more often than if they were simply moving about in solution and making chance encounters. It serves as a gathering place where chemicals may meet and unite.

Moreover, a little bit of catalyst can go a long way. Once the chemical reaction is completed the new compound is detached from the catalyst particle, flies off, and leaves the reactive sites vacant again. The particle is ready to promote further reactions. A catalyst not only speeds processes, but speeds them without changing itself. Although a great deal happens because of it, not much happens to it.

Such substances are not new in the universe. They may be found wherever matter, inanimate or animate or somewhere in between, is shaping itself into patterns. They are stepping up reactions that will bring life to a lifeless planet and, at the same time, they are at work in the stars of near and remote galaxies—and in the sun. At the core of the sun, protons, the nuclei of hydrogen atoms, are combining to

97

form helium and these processes also depend on collisions and meetings. Catalysts of a kind help increase reaction rates in solar gases as they do in less violent terrestrial waters.

The earth's early catalysts evolve along with other substances. They become more complex and more efficient in speeding up the pace of synthesis, until some of them can increase the rates of reactions by as much as a million times. Such reactions begin to flourish in the chemical struggle for existence. They flourish at the expense of reactions which may require the same starting or intermediate materials, but which have less efficient catalysts or none at all. Eventually the other reactions fade into insignificance or die out entirely. It is as if one company among a group of rival manufacturers managed to discover a new process and drive its competitors off the market. Competition takes place at the molecular level too, and continual weeding out and selection.

Something vaguely familiar is under way. It resembles events which took place long ago in prestellar space, processes developing among enormous clouds of unshaped gas. Then portions of the clouds swirled together in great rotating eddies and condensed, and the condensations were galaxies and stars. Then it was gas which began thickening and gave rise ultimately to starlight and solid stuff.

Now there are lesser swirlings, gentle eddies and condensations in water, fluid evolvings. Now there are new and more varied and complex substances. Matter, always on the move, concentrates in little patches and enters cycles of chain reactions. The reactions continue as long as they can. They feed off available material and stop when local supplies of the material are depleted, and perhaps start up again elsewhere in other patches. A persisting, cell-less, inanimate metabolism. Things undergo a slow warming up, like coals starting to glow—or like organic reactions inside a hayrick which becomes hotter and hotter and will eventually break into flame. A kind of spontaneous combustion will take place in the waters of the earth. But, as one investigator emphasizes, "a combustion that builds up instead of breaking down."

Still there is nothing much to see. The precursors of life slip quietly into the flow of things. Here, in a zone of concentrated stuff, another out-of-the-way place, an unusual variety of molecule appears. It is a long-chain molecule made up of many links and twisted into a helix or spiral-staircase structure. It moves in waters populated with links or groups of links on the loose, extra parts that have not been assembled. The helix begins to uncoil at one end like a frayed thread, and some of the extra parts drift to the free end and fasten themselves there.

The process continues. As the coil unwinds, more parts find places where they attach themselves and line up and link together. Another long-chain molecule is forming. One pattern and the beginning of another, but the building is never finished. There is a stirring, a change in the environment. The water becomes slightly cooler or a bit more acid, and that is enough to stop the linkings and the lining up. Something has flared up. A small flame has flickered and died away, like a candle in the wind.

Another zone, perhaps in the same pool or in a near-by pool or a thousand miles away. Perhaps at about the same time, or a century or two later. There is no hurry ever, anywhere. Matter makes many false starts and runs into many dead ends as it evolves, and time is ample. Another helix begins uncoiling, other parts attach themselves to the loose end and line up and hook together. Other changes, other failures, other flickerings and dying-outs. But at some time and in some place, or perhaps in a number of places at once, there is a chemical flicker that does not pass.

This time the process is not halted. The process goes to

completion; a helix uncoils entirely. Extra parts, groups of atoms in patterns, find places where they can fasten along the whole length of the uncoiling molecule. They join to create a superpattern. A second long chain detaches itself as a single unit. It twists into a second helix, a duplicate of the first. The links in the new helix are the same kinds of links that make up the parent helix, and they are arranged in the same order.

Organic reproduction has begun. Soon there are many uncoilings and many linkings and swarms of helixes. The original helix and its duplicate each serve as a pattern for the formation of still another helix. Now we have a total of four coiled molecules, and each of them produces a duplicate and the numbers start piling up—eight, sixteen, thirty-two, and so on. After twenty consecutive duplications there are more than a million helixes, after fifty steps, more than a million billion.

An observer would notice nothing spectacular. Perhaps only a slight cloudiness in the water. But reproduction has begun and it is here to stay. It is like a weak, cool blue sputtering which becomes a flame and then many flames. This fire of breeding molecules is not alive. Not yet. It does not yet have the trappings of life, but it has the essence. It spreads and it will spread further, and evolve. All living things, including ourselves, are to be the descendants of those spiral patterns.

This is one version of what may have happened. We are reasonably sure about the general drift of things. Starting with very simple compounds, some of the substance of earth evolved into more and more complex patterns, until the most complex were coiled molecules that reproduce. But the processes behind it all are not obvious ones. Records exist before the coming of fossils and hieroglyphics, information about primeval chemistry locked in rock crystals. Information revealed only by expert deciphering.

PRECURSORS OF LIFE—
REPRODUCING COILS

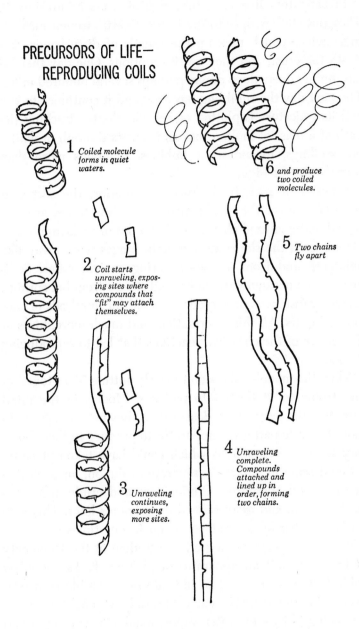

1 Coiled molecule forms in quiet waters.

2 Coil starts unraveling, exposing sites where compounds that "fit" may attach themselves.

3 Unraveling continues, exposing more sites.

4 Unraveling complete. Compounds attached and lined up in order, forming two chains.

5 Two chains fly apart

6 and produce two coiled molecules.

Investigators live near the edge of a crater in Hawaii. They put stethoscopes to the heaving earth, tremor-measuring devices which pick up the sounds of disturbances beneath the crust, and they await eruptions. One day there is a rumbling deep, deep down, perhaps several hundred miles. The next day the rumbling has risen and it continues to rise and its trajectory is plotted on seismic charts—tracking the path of a mass of molten rock as it bursts through in white-hot wellings, incandescent bubbles, fountains more than seventy stories high.

Samples of rock fresh from the interior, the sort that spurted all over the world in more restless times, are dissected and analyzed chemically. Samples of rock from other places, from the slopes of mountain ranges worn away like old teeth and from jungles covering ancient cities. Sediments from ocean floors, waters and steams from hot springs, organic substances preserved in crystal for hundreds of millions of years. All this information, and much more, hints at the nature of the chemical reactions that led to reproducing things.

Then the model-makers go to work, putting ideas together and trying to fit them into patterns. Models in the mind first. And the patterns of ideas lead as they must to action, to more tangible patterns—apparatus to produce in the laboratory small-scale reactions which could have taken place on a grand scale in nature. A separate evolution, an evolution of ideas and apparatus. Crude ideas and crude apparatus to start with, and more refined experiments later. This evolution has hardly started yet, even in our times.

About five years ago a graduate student at the University of Chicago built an apparatus of globular flasks and glass tubing. It was designed to indicate one possible course of events in one possible early atmosphere, an atmosphere consisting chiefly of water vapor, ammonia, hydrogen and methane or marsh gas. The water boiled in a large flask, and hydrogen and methane gases bubbled through it. The mix circulated for a week past a crackling spark which discharged at a peak of 60,000 volts.

A model of lightning in primeval skies. "The water in the flask became noticeably pink after the first day, and by the end of the week the solution was deep red and turbid." Changing color, a sign of substance in transition, in this case a sign of synthesis. The student analyzed the red solution and found that some of the simple starting compounds had joined and reorganized themselves into a variety of larger molecules. Among other things, the flashing spark had formed about half a dozen amino acids, the units that make up proteins.

One experiment, one model, out of hundreds. Variations on a theme, tests at other laboratories involving different possible atmospheres and different sources of energy—ultraviolet rays, heat and radioactivity instead of electrical discharges. The tests yield similar results, the synthesis of many organic substances under primitive conditions. Further research indicates how more complex intermediate compounds might have formed, and globules and catalysts and systems of catalysts. Exploring reactions and reaction rates and possibilities. Sifting through new evidence as it accumulates, until possibilities become probabilities.

Another model of a different type, perhaps the most important model ever built in the history of the life sciences. At about the time of the Chicago experiment two investigators at Cambridge University in England set out to determine the structure of an enormously complex molecule. A giant molecule representing a compound with a formidable name, desoxyribonucleic acid, or DNA for short. DNA is found in every living cell. It is the material out of which heredity-transmitting genes are made, and slight changes in its structure may lead to cancer and other diseases. It also provides clues to the possible structure of "breeding" molecules on earth.

A great deal of painstaking research by investigators in

103

other laboratories lay behind the effort to build a DNA model. Workers at King's College in London had spent years extracting the compound from cells, carefully dipping glass rods into thick, gooey preparations and drawing them out to form crystalline filaments of DNA. They used x-ray methods to study the structure of the filaments. The rays bend in passing through crystals, and the patterns of their bending suggest how atoms are arranged in crystal lattices. Many x-ray photographs had indicated that the DNA molecule is coiled in some way. Furthermore, biochemists in the United States, Germany and other countries had discovered the less complex compounds that go into the assembly of the molecule.

The Cambridge investigators first constructed simple models of these parts, pieces of a scientific jigsaw puzzle in three dimensions. One of the pieces was a flat sheet of metal cut into a nine-sided geometrical pattern with four rods sticking out at the sides. It indicated the way atoms are arranged in a compound called adenine, the rods being atomic side groups attached to the central structure of the molecule. The adenine piece looked something like this:

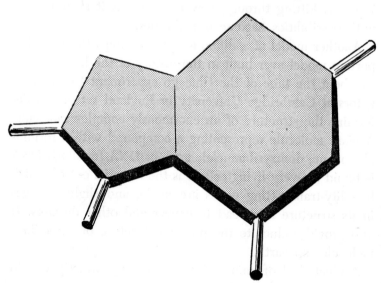

Another piece was cut into the same general shape, with five rods instead of four, and represented a related compound, guanine. Two smaller pieces also resembled each other; both hexagons having different arrangements of rods, these represented compounds called thymine and cytosine. The four substances are members of a class known to chemists as "bases." There were two other kinds of pieces, each with appropriate rods—a pentagon-shaped sugar piece and a cross-shaped phosphate piece.

Half a dozen metal pieces. We can think of them as molecules enlarged hundreds of millions of times and built precisely to scale, models of atoms in spatial configurations. Only half a dozen different pieces, but many copies of each piece. The problem was to put them all together into one great pattern, to make a single symmetrical DNA model out of the smaller models. By comparison, tackling the most complicated jigsaw puzzle ever devised would be a kindergarten game.

It took the Cambridge investigators about a month to solve the problem. "We spent most of the time getting nowhere, concentrating chiefly on various arrangements of the sugar and phosphate pieces." Then they hit on the idea of pairing the bases, a large one with a small one, in just the right way, and from there on things proceeded swiftly. The last stages of the problem required three days and a good part of three nights.

The completed model is a master pattern of connected pieces, resembling a modernistic sculpture or an abstract mobile. It is so elaborate that at first sight it appears confusing and disorderly. But the design and the symmetry become evident as you keep on looking, the pattern emerges gradually. The model consists of adenine-thymine and guanine-cytosine pairs wrapped around a long axis or backbone of alternate sugar and phosphate units. The pieces fit neatly into place. They form a double helix, a system of two woven-together coils.

Molecules of this sort, twisted like submicroscopic confetti, are packed inside the nucleus of every cell. They are the physical stuff, the genes, which we inherit from our parents, and which our parents inherit from remote generations. They direct the shaping of a single fertilized egg cell into a full-grown organism of many cells. They duplicate themselves over and over again, so that each one of the many cells, and there may be trillions, has the same genes as the original egg. Inherited DNA molecules uncoil, reproduce and give rise to new double helixes which thereby insure the passage of hereditary traits to future generations.

One more model, chemicals in solution, and a surprise. The solution was prepared in a glass vessel at Washington University in St. Louis and contained parts of DNA, compounds of the four bases with sugars and phosphates. It also contained a biological catalyst or enzyme, which speeds synthesis. To this brew of unassembled parts, investigators added a dash of a "primer" to start things going, a tiny amount of DNA. The glass vessel promptly became a breeding place, a site of active coming together. The parts assembled to form large numbers of new molecules in the image of the added DNA molecules, and by replenishing the starting substances, unlimited quantities of DNA could be produced.

The surprise was a fact discovered during the course of the experiment. A simpler molecule including only two bases, adenine and thymine, will reproduce in a similar way. Such evidence suggests that perhaps the first organic molecules that reproduced were crude Neanderthal versions of DNA. Genes of a kind, but genes strictly on their own. Molecules which came before nuclei or cells or organisms and floated free in ancient waters and reproduced to pass their characteristics on to later generations of molecules. The beginning was a world of naked genes.

So reconstructing through models a past several billion

years old is not entirely guesswork. And there will be less guesswork in the future. Not long ago investigators from many nations met in Moscow for an International Symposium on the Origin of Life. They received a cablegram from biologists in India who could not attend and, as a joke, gave this reason: "This is to inform you that living matter has just been synthesized in our laboratory. Best wishes for the success of the symposium." A reporter failed to get the joke. There were excited headlines throughout the world about the creation of life in a test tube, and denials and explanations.

To some scientists at the meeting, however, it was something more than a joke that misfired. It was a small-scale preview of how the world would react to the real news. Sooner or later, perhaps within a decade or so, there will be similar headlines—and no denials. The laboratory synthesis of living matter is no daydream. It will probably happen, and the first steps will probably make use of substances that may have existed at some stage of chemical evolution in the primeval soup. The odds are that it will involve DNA-like molecules, the reproducing things from which all creatures and species were to come.

The Coming

of Cells

7

WE pick up our story in waters swarming with self-duplicating molecules. They represent the most advanced stage of evolution yet attained on earth, the highest species of terrestrial matter. Patterns of thousands and thousands of symmetrically organized atoms, complex spiral-woven structures, they will themselves become incorporated into—and guide the shaping of—far more complex patterns. For patterns do not and cannot remain indefinitely the same. They are swept up in a process like bits of bark and leaves and roots in a mountain stream. The process can either shape matter into increasingly elaborate forms, or stop altogether. And it does not stop.

Wherever self-duplicating molecules arise, they spread swiftly. In any region, the first such molecules are like the first little sliding snows on the high slopes of a mountain. Small sheets of snow slide at the start and unsettle deeper and greater snows on the way down. The sliding grows and catches up more snow and the sounds of sliding mount to a roar and there is an avalanche of loosened snows. The roars of chemical avalanches are imminent in many pools and muddy places on the primeval earth. Reproduction is gathering momentum.

But we need something more. Reproduction alone is not enough for evolution. Crystals learned the trick long ago, and still they do not evolve. A single crystal forming in a solution of many substances may act as a sort of seed. Under the proper conditions it "selects" out of the entire solution only those substances which are needed to produce crystals like itself. The substances are organized into another crystal and then into glittering masses of crystals, and the process may continue until the solution is filled with crystal images of the original.

This is what happened during the deep-freeze stage when the earth and other planets were condensing out of the solar nebula. Crystals take shape when molten rock cools and hardens, as it did to make the earth's crust and as it does now on the slopes of active volcanoes. Crystals take shape in the atmosphere, and the formation of little needles of ice precedes the coming of snow or rain.

Crystals reproduce everywhere, in showers of symmetrical patterns. They do not always reproduce exactly. There may be flaws in crystals, imperfections which spoil symmetries. But the flaws do not affect future generations in any significant way. Take a cube-shaped crystal which has a certain type of uneven edge or a slightly warped surface. If it reproduces itself, the resulting crystals do not as a rule show this particular flaw. Most of them will be "corrected." They will be perfectly regular cubes, the sort that are pictured in geometry textbooks. This means that, strictly speaking, the parent cube does not breed true to itself. It breeds true to, or toward, the canonical pattern of the textbook cube—and away from random imperfections.

So the world of crystals is a static, stand-pat, stay-put world where essential patterns are fixed forever. Random flaws are incidental and tend to be ironed out and do not leave their marks systematically on future crystals. New patterns will never develop from the old ones. Crystals resist change the hard way, putting up a stiff front, building solid and rigid structures, brittle-hard mineral stuff and flints and monoliths. They have no future, or rather, their future is predictable. They grow and reproduce, but only to generate more rigidities of the same kind. We know what they will look like eons from now. Crystals forming like gems from today's lavas have the same shapes as those which solidified from lavas millions of centuries ago. Evolution does not lie that way.

The future belongs to more flexible things, to things that can give way and ride with punches and resist change by changing. The future belongs to the earth's new reproducing molecules, coiled structures which are also crystals of a sort and may also have random "flaws." But these flaws are not ironed out. These flaws or mutations are reproduced, passed on from generation to generation. And the secret of all evolution is that inherited imperfections may be useful.

Say that a single helical molecule organizes substances into an image of itself. The result is that twin molecules exist, and the process may continue until the total has increased to about a thousand. Out of the thousand only one may be a freak, differing from the others in some small way. It is a mutation which goes ahead on its own. It organizes the same substances, or most of the same substances plus one or two new ones, into a new coiled molecule like itself—and almost but not quite like the other molecules around it.

The mutation, the new pattern, is not lost and keeps on multiplying. Now we have two races or strains of reproducing molecules. Eventually the original strain gives rise to another kind of self-duplicating mutation and so does the second strain and soon there will be many many strains. If single molecules take a minute to make duplicates of themselves, the total population could double every minute. So an hour would be time enough for sixty successive doublings or generations, the equivalent of fifteen hundred years of human generations, and time enough to yield about a billion billion offspring. Reproduction rolls along at a fantastic pace.

Imagine an automatic factory which makes intricate parts and assembles them into model airplanes. If the models are all alike except for minor flaws, if this is a conventional assembly line, we have an analogy with the process of reproduction for ordinary mineral crystals. Imagine another automatic factory, a factory which works with an insane and yet systematic inefficiency. It starts by turning out airplane models to a certain design, but at some point a mistake occurs. An off-shape wing or tail fin is produced. Suddenly two assembly lines exist, one turning out the original model and the other turning out models with the off-shape part.

By the time a whole multitude of mistakes have accumulated, this factory will be an interesting place. Its many assembly lines will manufacture a variety of weird and unusual models, most of which could never fly. But a few of the models might actually fly, and some of them might even fly better than the original model. This factory can be compared with the workings of molecules which mutate and reproduce their mutations.

Such molecules survive when survival seems impossible. Such molecules evolve. Here in a body of water not far from sea and surf is a great population of self-duplicating helixes, a large number of different strains. One strain is doing best of all. It is a highly successful chemical species, a master breed that dominates its environment. This pool represents a frontier, a virgin territory as rich in natural resources as the New World was when the pioneers first entered it. To

111

reproduce its kind the master breed needs, among other things, the two chemical bases adenine and thymine—and the substances are everywhere in abundance.

Yet the master breed is doomed. All systems, reproducing and nonreproducing, exist in a restless universe where emergency follows emergency. Many emergencies can be traced to one simple fact. It is of the nature of things that natural resources are used up, at least locally. Gases are used up in forming spiral Milky Ways, stars among the spirals, and planets among the stars. The dwindling of supplies influences the evolution of matter in space—the careers of galaxies, the bursting and shrinking of stars to white dwarfs, the futures of suns and their satellites. It is the same in primeval waters on earth.

The master breed is doomed, because it faces an unavoidable scarcity. It multiplies too rapidly for its own good. Its pool, its world, is becoming overexploited, overpopulated. There is a food shortage, a famine. Supplies of adenine and thymine are limited and dwindling. Adenine is the first to go, and the master breed goes with it. At this stage and in this place reproduction would come to a complete halt if the master breed were the only breed, if by some miracle complex helixes could only make faithful likenesses of themselves. In a changing world, if reproduction were perfect, and if some imperfections were not useful, reproduction would cease utterly.

This is what actually happens in a great many places. But it does not happen everywhere, and it does not happen here. In these waters the spotlight shifts. It shifts to a lesser breed, a strain of metabolic weaklings or underdogs that have been multiplying all along in the shadow of the master breed, a strain of freaks. The mutated molecules happen to be capable of synthesizing the missing food substance. They do not need adenine ready-made, prefabricated. They can

112

build it out of two other compounds which are simpler and in greater abundance. So another dominant breed arises and reproduction continues.

A new emergency comes later, and a new development. One of the two compounds which can be combined to produce adenine begins to dwindle. That puts a premium on any strain that can synthesize this compound from simpler and more abundant substances, and by this time the number of different strains is so large that one of them has the necessary qualifications. Now a sort of symbiosis takes place, the first joining of its kind, a joining which is fruitful and mutually parasitic. The new strain can use abundant substances to make one of the parts of adenine, but perhaps it cannot make adenine as efficiently as the other strain which is specialized to do so. The other strain can make adenine but not the dwindling part.

There are so many self-duplicating molecules in these waters that the next logical step occurs. Members of the two strains meet and hook up. They form a firm union, a larger two-piece coil. Eventually perhaps things work out so that each of them controls a different chemical reaction and supplies the other's deficiency. Furthermore, they multiply together to yield new generations of single units composed of two mutations.

Systems of many mutations, huge molecules like those of DNA, come with subsequent emergencies, with the passing of time and the coming of new mutations and new shortages and new extinctions and dominances. Sooner or later thymine becomes scarce and is synthesized from simpler compounds, and the simpler compounds themselves become scarce and are synthesized from still simpler substances. And all the time more and more complex systems of mutations arise, for the simpler the starting products, the more steps or chemical reactions in the synthesis. There are longer

113

and more intricately made reproducing molecules, patterns of patterns, patterns of coils and coils within coils and coiled coils. A world of subtly and invisibly interwoven spirals.

The parts of sections of every highly evolved helix guide the synthesis of some of the specific substances needed to construct the whole system. They work together to shape raw materials, unorganized substances, into patterns of reproducing things. The trend is toward a greater and greater degree of self-sufficiency. Coiled molecules rely less on the presence of rare and complex compounds, elaborate prefabricated parts, and the risk of shortages and famines is reduced. Reproduction becomes more and more independent of accidents, of declining supplies of building materials. It is like an expanding industrial plant which once obtained steel parts ready-made from different companies and is now beginning to make the parts from crude ones treated in its own furnaces and mills.

Somewhere along the line there is another noteworthy development. Some of these molecular factories become enclosed. They build walls around themselves, mark themselves off from the rest of the world, and exert more control over their immediate environment. Some of them may turn out substances not needed for image-making. Substances left over from the synthesis of essential compounds are released into the water as wastes, perhaps including proteins and fatty materials which combine to form spherical coatings.

The coatings may be layered structures consisting of a film of protein between two films of fat, like a slice of meat in a sandwich. They resemble the globules formed and dispersed like bubbles in earlier times. One difference is that the new globules reproduce. Another is that they may persist for longer periods, because they are built and restored from within. Molecules at work inside the globules provide a steady supply of fats and proteins.

A POSSIBLE STAGE BETWEEN
DNA MOLECULES AND CELLS

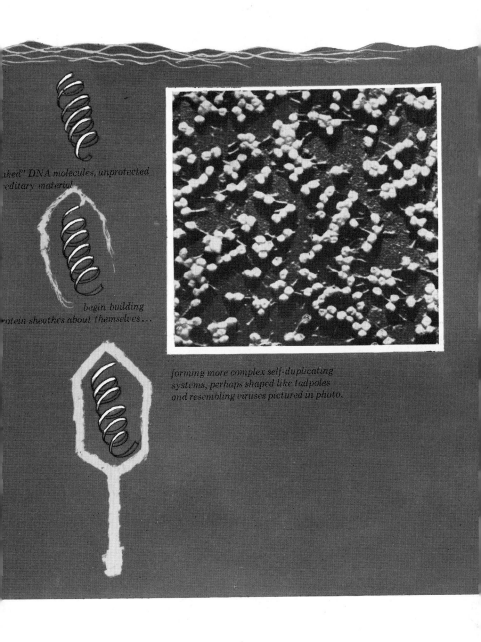

...ked" DNA molecules, unprotected ...editary material

begin building ...otein sheathes about themselves...

forming more complex self-duplicating systems, perhaps shaped like tadpoles and resembling viruses pictured in photo.

ANCIENT CELLS

along northern shore of Lake Superior in rocks of Gunflint Iron Formation, Ontario, Canada, investigators have found fossil cells between one and two billion years old pictured below in microphotographs

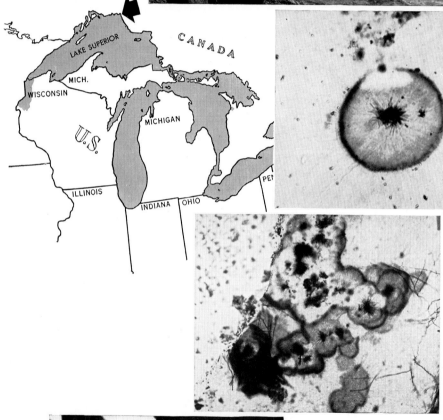

For a time walled and naked systems exist together. But probably not for long. Walled systems have many advantages in a changing environment where there are many dangers. For example, the sun's ultraviolet rays are intense and produce quantities of an extremely reactive substance when they strike the water. This compound can destroy other materials explosively, including nucleic acids like DNA out of which reproducing helixes may be made. It is a deadly "poison," and perhaps coiled molecules inside capsules are better protected from it than naked molecules. In any case, they multiply more efficiently, giving rise to more molecules which make coatings or membranes—and, in turn, give rise to more reproducing offspring. Eventually they overwhelm and drive out their capsule-less relatives by the sheer weight of numbers.

The membranes around reproducing things serve as selective sieves which allow useful substances to enter and keep out many poisons. The capsules represent a new order of complexity in the pattern-forming process that is evolution. But not all biologists would agree that life has appeared, that the moment has arrived. In fact, *the* moment never arrives. Suddenness is not nature's method, at this point in the history of matter. Some astronomers and physicists feel they need a sudden event, the bursting of a compact mass of atoms or cosmic egg, to explain the origin of the expanding universe. Biologists do not need a "big bang" for their beginnings.

We are in a borderline zone, a shadow land on the way to higher forms, and life comes slowly out of the shadows. Inanimate substance evolves to animate substance by such small steps that in this region it would be arbitrary to try to say where one leaves off and the other begins. Evolution resembles a passing from early morning to dawn, from plain to foothill, from suburb to city. New states of matter emerge gradually. Reproducing capsules are alive or not alive depending on what investigator you talk with and how he defines life.

The capsules are devices designed chiefly for the protection and servicing of the all-important coiled molecules inside. These particles now carry the entire burden of evolution. They are the indispensable agents in a growing system of organizations. If they disappear, evolution will cease on earth. If they prosper, nothing can prevent the emergence of new forms. They are treasures of a very special type, the heritage of all that may come. They are the future, and they must be preserved at all costs. They preserve themselves partly by shaping other materials in their own images, by passing their features along. These molecules are no longer naked heredity-transmitting units, naked genes, but shielded genes whose remote descendants—enclosed in more elaborate shells—will spread over the face of the earth and eventually make their way to other planets.

Genes also preserve themselves by changing continually, or mutating. Mutations make the construction of new shells possible. Many strains of reproducing bodies appear, and most of them have no particular advantages for surviving or evolving. Most of them exist feebly and ultimately pass away. But some reach out and capture a fragment of the outside world, a tiny piece of the environment, and claim it for their own. They do this by building a second wall, an outer membrane surrounding not only the gene capsule but also compounds which may be organized into more genes. There is a central enclosure or nucleus containing genes and an outlying region containing raw materials or foods. The nucleus is like a farmhouse. The outlying region with its outer wall is like fenced-in acres of farmland. Both have been carved out of a wilderness.

This is a cell, or the forerunner of cells. We have reached the next stage, for no matter how life is defined, cells are alive. The earliest forms exploit fresh possibilities to the hilt.

116

But, again, they spread too swiftly. They are still living off the land, still consumers rather than producers. Everything that has happened so far depends on the presence in primeval waters of ready-made materials. Life is drawing on a capital of organic stuff accumulated over past ages. At this time the stuff of life is relatively simple. More of it may be forming spontaneously in many places, but not nearly fast enough to keep up with the booming reproduction of cells and the booming demand for more and more foods.

Again, it is a matter of overpopulation and approaching scarcity, approaching extinction by famine. Again, reproducing things appear to be heading for an inglorious end. And, again, the future is not that grim. It seldom is. The time when nature seems to have exhausted her possibilities, when she seems to have painted herself into a corner, is exactly the time to watch out for a new beginning. Life the upstart seems to be scheduled for a brief career, like a shooting star that puts its streak into the night sky as it disintegrates and vanishes. But this streaking thing is no shooting star. It flares up again and again and again.

More imperfect and inherited duplications, more mutations. Among them are new strains of cells which use one of the very simplest and most abundant compounds of all, carbon dioxide. They also use common water and radiation from the sun, visible light, which is more intense than ultraviolet light, and minerals. The strains perform their syntheses with the aid of the green pigment chlorophyll, a light-trap which absorbs sunshine and puts it to work. Genes have produced something resembling an electric eye or photocell, a crystalline element in protoplasm which converts light into electricity. Feeble electrical currents play a part in building sugars and starches from carbon dioxide and water and sunlight in the process known as photosynthesis. From these compounds and from minerals the cell can make proteins and a host of other organic substances.

Such single-cell plants do more than merely use substances of the environment. They gradually bring about large-scale changes in the environment itself. Up to this point the earth's atmosphere has contained little if any free oxygen, far too little to support life as we know it. Now oxygen begins to appear in the waters and atmosphere. Primitive cells "exhale" oxygen. It is a by-product of photosynthesis, a discarded material thrown off as plants grow and spread. Each cell contributes only a tiny amount, but as reproduction accelerates and numbers increase the total quantity becomes larger and larger. The environment is being polluted, contaminated with the wastes of living things.

This means the extinction of a great many strains designed to live without oxygen. Like people suffocating in an airtight room, they succumb to their own accumulating poisons. But other strains survive because they happen to have the right genes, the right mutations. They are immune or resistant to oxygen. In time some surviving strains readjust so completely that they not only resist oxygen contamination but actually thrive on the element.

They prefer oxygen to carbon dioxide, and consume it as a source of energy. For them the poison has become a kind of food. They are single-cell animals using a waste plant product. And, one of their wastes is carbon dioxide, which plants may use to grow and produce more oxygen. The living world is developing into one vast self-contained and self-perpetuating system. The most basic problem of food shortages has been solved.

We have come a long way in evolution. There are many theories about how reproduction went from the submicroscopic to the microscopic level, from reproducing molecule or naked gene to cell. No theory is completely satisfactory, which is hardly surprising. A cell is a pattern, a growing and changing pattern directed by the synchronized interactions of self-duplicating subpatterns. A community of hundreds of genes. As far as biochemical complexity is concerned, the difference between a naked gene and a cell is greater than the difference between a cell and an ape.

So the record has many gaps and we deduce what we can from models and experiments—for example, from more detailed research on our models of the structure of the nucleic acid DNA. The earth houses an estimated two million species of living things. Every one of them has genes, and every gene is made up of DNA. Every gene is part of a double helix which may consist of millions of coils or turnings. Furthermore, the basic structure of the helix is always the same. It includes four and only four bases—usually adenine (A), guanine (G), thymine (T), and cytosine (C). In the helix, adenine always joins up with guanine and thymine with cytosine to form A-G and T-C pairs.

In other words, the genes of every species are parts of the same broad pattern composed of the same bases and paired in the same way. The differences among species are determined largely by different sequences of these pairs along great coils of DNA. Each species has its unique genes, its unique chain of joined pairs, its unique sequence. If we knew all the details of all existing sequences, we could take a single DNA molecule and unravel it and tell what species it belongs to.

We could read off the sequences like dots and dashes or ticker tape. A sequence starting "A-G, A-G, T-C, A-G, T-C . . ." might represent an ameba; "T-C, T-C, A-G, T-C, A-G . . ." a shark; "A-G, T-C, T-C, T-C, A-G . . ." a man. We could even identify individuals of the same species. The sequences for two human beings who differ in eye color and other inheritable traits would differ in a corresponding number of places (although not in as many places as in the case of two individuals each representing a different species).

Genes are blueprints of a sort. They contain inherited codes, specifications more definite and detailed than those

119

of any do-it-yourself handbook. They specify a precise set of chemical reactions in a precise order. More concretely, they control the processes whereby proteins and other organic compounds are organized into tissues and complete organisms. The control is exerted indirectly, probably by bringing about the synthesis of reaction-speeding catalysts of life, or enzymes. The quantity of "information" contained in a set of genes is enormous. For a human being it amounts to more information than could be printed in 250 volumes each the size of Webster's Unabridged Dictionary. Nature has crammed her messages into DNA molecules. Compared with this feat, engraving the Lord's Prayer on the head of a pin is sky writing.

The duplication of DNA molecules, the duplication of a set of genes, is like the copying of a long and detailed message in code. A mutation is a mistake in the copy. The mistake may be very small, but it can have serious effects. For example, investigators believe that one type of human anemia results from a change of only a single A-G or T-C pair in a coiled sequence of many millions of pairs—a pair concerned with the manufacture of the red blood pigment hemoglobin. Such changes may also produce mental disorders and other diseases. Things would go badly if genes did not reproduce themselves with reasonable accuracy.

Plenty of evidence indicates the importance of occasional mutations. There are no known examples of naked genes or naked gene systems like those that may have existed in earlier times. But we do have examples of the next possible stage, reproducing capsules which are much simpler than cells. Viruses, bodies responsible for such diseases as infantile paralysis and smallpox, resemble nuclei operating on their own or nuclei without cells. Some of them consist almost entirely of pure DNA, pure genes, enclosed in a coating of protein. The smallest one is so small that ten thousand billion would fit easily into a sphere no bigger across than the letter "o."

Infection is a battle to the death between competing hereditary materials. One type of virus is shaped like a tadpole or a sperm. It backs into its victim, a cell, so that its tail penetrates the outer part of the cell membrane. Then it becomes an animated hypodermic needle. Coiled DNA molecules from its head are injected into the cell through the hollow tail, and generally take over the genetic apparatus of the cell. They prevent the cell's DNA molecules from reproducing. They monopolize available raw materials to build virus DNA, virus genes and more viruses. After about twenty minutes the infected cell bursts. Out of its substance, like maggots from meat gone bad, come more than a hundred new viruses complete with heads and tails, and ready to infect other cells.

Viruses may not kill at once. Their genetic material can enter the innermost citadel of a cell, the nucleus which holds genes or DNA. Instead of doing damage right away, the invaders may stay put in the nucleus, multiply when the cell multiplies and be passed or smuggled from generation to generation like conventional genes. Indeed, during the passages they cannot be distinguished from cell genes. They may live dormant for generations and then go into action, reproducing in large numbers and escaping into the outer world. The difference between viruses and genes, infection and heredity, is not always obvious. From one standpoint viruses are genes on the loose, free-swimming packets of nucleic acids such as DNA.

Viruses live and breed on cells. But virus-like particles may once have been independent agents, free-lancers rather than parasites. Perhaps they were "swallowed" by early cells. Some mutants may have accepted peaceful coexistence and actually become parts of cell nuclei, functioning indefinitely as hereditary material. Others may have fought back by multiplying inside their enemies and breaking out to breed anew.

In any case, viruses on earth today survive and spread in

such ways. During 1918 mutants of influenza viruses broke loose and enjoyed a period of spectacular gains. That was the time of the influenza epidemic which hit its peak after World War I and killed at least fifteen million people before running its course. One species' meat may be another's poison. Another successful mutant, fortunately less lethal, has been responsible for more recent outbreaks of Asian flu.

Other organisms that can cause infection, bacteria, may be descendants of the first true cells. Some of them live without oxygen, by fermentation, the same process that turns grape juice into wine and rye into whisky or vodka. Such cells could have multiplied even in the days when the world was deficient in free oxygen. Also, bacteria provide a rough model of the rise of oxygen-consuming strains. In the laboratory, colonies of tuberculosis germs may be exposed to the antibiotic streptomycin, a poison as deadly to them as oxygen must have been to the original fermenting cells. The drug is an efficient killer, and, in test-tube concentrations, may destroy 999,999,997 out of every billion germs.

That is not good enough. The three survivors are mutants that happen to be resistant to streptomycin. They may not do too well. They may multiply more slowly than they would under normal conditions. But succeeding generations include many mutants, some of which are even more resistant to the drug. Finally, it is possible to produce strains which have changed so much that they flourish in the presence of high concentrations of streptomycin. Indeed, some strains cannot live without it. Primitive cells may have come to depend on oxygen in a similar manner. This is also how antibiotics can produce drug-resistant germs in patients, and how insects become immune to the effects of chemical sprays. Moreover, as we shall see, it is the main process behind all biological evolution—behind Darwin's so-called struggle for survival.

We do not know when life appeared on earth. But current

studies are tending to push the beginning further and further back into time. Patterns in rocks from the Gunflint Iron Formation in Ontario, Canada. Circular patterns "surrounded by the remains of what is interpreted as a gelatinous sheath," filaments of protoplasm turned to coal, amber-brown traces of globules that were once alive—all etched so clearly that they can be identified as fossil plants, algae and fungi; and cells with tails for swimming. These rocks are about two billion years old.

Still older rocks contain the same kinds of patterns. The oldest known rock comes from Southern Rhodesia—a pebble of granite dating back nearly three billion years. Three and a half billion years ago limestones existed which look exactly like limestones being formed by algae today, although we have no direct proof that algae built the ancient deposits. In other words, according to recent evidence, such organisms were flourishing at least three billion years ago. Yet they were not the first cells; presumably bacteria preceded them in terrestrial waters. Even before that there may have been virus-like bodies and, still earlier, systems of self-duplicating molecules without protective membranes. These origins recede into a past that has not yet been dated.

Life arises early in primeval times. Even at the earliest stages, even among single cells, we have many strains and many patterns. But the basic patterns which shape everything else are the patterns of genes, the intricate coded helixes of molecules like DNA. They represent an entirely new kind of organized matter. They reproduce. But they also slip up and make copying mistakes, and the sins of the parents are passed on, and that is at once their failing and their glory. Mutations are possibilities, an unending source of novelty, the source of the variety that is the spice of life.

Nature, the opportunist supreme, is confronted with the bare fact of random and unavoidable imperfections—and makes a major virtue of necessity. In the long run the imperfections are not obstacles or handicaps to limp along with as well as possible. They are transformed. They become powerful and positive and creative forces. It is almost as if bits of the original chaos had been trapped somewhere inside the lattice cages of helixes, chaos preserved and controlled and used. The irrational finds its place and is domesticated, and helps generate higher levels of order and complexity. Trapped randomness is the essence of organic evolution.

This is something we do well to note. It is the sign of life, of deep-seated and fundamental changes. An assurance of continual stirrings that come from within and keep coming. Peace, in the sense of staying the same, is impossible. Genes would spoil it, even in an unchanging world. Even in an ideally adjusted place, an Eden. Changes would occur even in a perfect environment, where the weather was lovely all the time and food supplies were unlimited and nothing ever hunted and fought and killed. Emergencies always arise inside reproducing things.

The inner emergencies are mutations and new combinations of genes. Freaks and sports that do not fit into established patterns. Upstarts which come from the best of families and are different simply because the making of images is not error-proof. Most of the mutants soon die out, and their impact is only temporary at best. But some of them persist and continue to disturb the peace, until another new and temporary peace is attained. These things would happen even in an Eden. The serpent was a mutation; all serpents are mutations. Genes have taken over the job of evolution.

Genes in

Action

8

MATTER is building itself from the ground up into hierarchies of many levels. Protons and electrons, chemical elements, molecules and crystals, genes, combinations of genes,
cells—each phase more subtle and more highly organized
than the one before it. It is like the times following the exploration of new lands, following the efforts of the trail blaz-
ers, when townships and boroughs and counties and states
arise where there once were only individuals and families
among wide forests and prairies. For the past, always simpler ways and simpler patterns and nostalgia; for the future,
always increasing complexity.

Single cells arise in a great variety of forms, ranging from
shapeless blobs to neat geometrical patterns. There are cells
resembling mosaic pieces or the colored-glass fragments of a
kaleidoscope: triangles, ovals, rods, hourglass and bottle-
shaped and tubular forms. Cells with spikes and cups and

funnels and spouts. Cells which enclose themselves in crystal cubicles of limestone, calcium shells having the same spiral patterns as snail shells.

These are gross features, microscopic structures representing the outward signs of far smaller structures, like the shape of a sculpture seen so far away that the details are lost. A single cell is an entire world, a submerged world in which a skin diver the size of an atom would find strange and wonderful formations—the seaweed jungles and coral reefs and undersea valleys and mountain ranges and seaweed-hidden places of the microcosm. A single cell viewed from within, from the central nucleus, would appear as an abstract architectural system of domes and globes and plates and crystalline fibers meshed and interlocking. At least that is how it would look if all the motions of all the parts were frozen, caught like a rocket in mid-flight, photographed with a time exposure of a millionth of a second or so. One frame of a high-speed motion picture.

A single cell, like the genes which guide its shaping, changes incessantly to resist change. Nothing stays the same, nothing but the essential thing, the form. All else is subsidiary, almost incidental. Stand at the crest of a waterfall, at the very edge where the water rushes most swiftly, curving downward in a sheet. As you watch, the water sweeps and roars past and falls away. The substance of this pattern drops over the edge continually. But that is only part of the process. It is steadily replenished by waters arriving from upriver, and the pattern remains. The curved pattern covering the edge and hanging at the edge like a suspended glass bow remains, a swirling and glimmering and persisting form.

All such patterns, whirlpools and flames and the funnels of cyclones and sunspots, share a quality with cells, a kind of metabolism in which the form endures while the content passes and is never the same. Work is always going on inside a cell, and not occasional patchwork or repairs or minor alterations. Everywhere molecules are being torn apart completely and rebuilt and torn apart again. Changes in primeval seas outside, depletions of available foods and shifts in acidity and temperature, threaten the existence of cells. Whole populations may be annihilated. Yet life rides out emergencies and continues, because changes inside cells continue.

The cell is a culmination of more than a billion years of chemical evolution, a culmination and another new beginning. Matter has not stopped condensing. Groups of cells come on the scene almost as soon as single cells. They come in many ways, often in a haphazard fashion, mainly because protoplasm has a tendency to form clumps, even though the forming may bring no particular benefits to members of the group. Bacteria stick together in chains and clusters. There are permanent colonies and transients which break up into individuals.

Oversized cells, dinosaurs for their day, lumber about, heavy with the burden of more than one nucleus. Some of them, like some corporations and government agencies, are too unwieldy to function efficiently. They do not survive. Others solve their problems of biochemical administration and perpetuate themselves. Still others develop into clumps of nuclei enclosed in separate outer membranes, clumps of smaller cells, colonies formed from within.

Many different kinds of colonies evolve in early waters. here in a region smaller than a raindrop is a hunting ground for primitive things. The hunters are tens of thousands of amebas crawling about and engulfing their prey, bacteria, in transparent tentacle-like extensions or pseudopods. Each ameba is out for itself alone. It is a fight to the finish with no holds barred, a swarm of freebooters, not a colony.

A change occurs gradually, so gradually that an observer might miss the first steps. Somewhere in the melee a few amebas stop feeding and stop crawling and join to form a sort of clot. A few more amebas move toward the little group, and then more and more. A self-accelerating process. The bigger the clot grows, the more cells it attracts. Something similar happened on a larger scale during the shaping of the solar system, when, under the attracting influence of gravitation, planetesimals fell toward dense centers and fused together into the earth. The amebas are attracted chemically, like flies to sugar or bloodhounds to a scent.

The clot becomes a fusing or condensing center, a gathering point for the members of the swarm. Amebas come toward the center as if drawn by a magnet. They resemble raindrops on a windowpane blown by the wind, bumping and forming larger droplets and rivulets. A mass migration, streams of living stuff all flowing inward to the meeting place, along spoke lines toward the hub of an invisible wheel.

Now no trace of the original swarm remains. In its place is a large blob of protoplasm, an ordered blob, an aggregate. And the aggregate moves as a single co-ordinated thing, a single cell which has a membrane of its own and moves on the membrane like a war tank on its tread. A new giant ameba swims through the water, veering and gliding and leaving behind it a trail as slimy as the trail of a slug. A giant ameba made up of all the stuff that once made up a hundred thousand individual cells. An organism which may be an inch or more long.

In certain respects the primitive organism is a model for the formation of all many-celled things. The whole becomes something more than the sum of its parts. Cells were once freebooters, rugged individualists. Like all rugged individualists, they resembled one another quite closely; in fact, they were practically identical. But they behave differently in groups. They begin to acquire significant differences, distinctive traits and individualities and patterns of behavior, only as members of a unified colony or population. They respond to organizing forces and take on special duties.

Groups of cells may form in another way. Perhaps a single

cell divides, but the two new cells fail to go their separate ways after division. Subsequent divisions take place and still there is no drifting apart. Instead we have a colony of cells all descended from the same parent and all moving through the water together like a cluster of galaxies or stars moving through space. Nature may have developed the division-of-labor principle out of such colonies.

Gradually a new kind of cell evolves, the "egg" or reproductive cell. It gives rise not only to things like itself but to an integrated living organism, a system made up of different kinds of specialists. Reproductive cells are like queen bees in hives. They alone are responsible for the perpetuation of the species. They contain the genes which will determine the shaping of organisms yet to come, the material necessary to continue the thread of life through millions and millions of future generations.

One type of colony, for example, is shaped like a ball. It contains hundreds or thousands of cells, but only about a dozen are the reproductive kind. Many of its cells have little "feet," tendrils which lash back and forth, natural oars or pedals. Distributed around the outer surface of the ball, they work in unison and roll the ball along through the water like a circular centipede. The colony also includes cells which do the feeding for the group, and detector cells which are sensitive to light and help in navigating. All the members of the colony are held together by strands of protoplasm, embedded in a three-dimensional lattice framework of filaments produced by another kind of cell.

The filament-makers may be descendants of cells that failed to divide properly. Perhaps a cell once became thinner and thinner around the middle, started pulling apart, and developed a wasp-waist or hourglass figure. A tug-of-war, with the protoplasm between stretching into a fine thread. But division never took place. This thread, this umbilical cord, never severed. A freak had arisen, like a pair of Siamese twins.

129

A failure of the most crucial sort, a failure of reproduction. In a world where survival depends utterly on efficient reproduction, nothing would appear to be more useless than such an abnormality. But nature may have exploited such freaks as she has many others.

Cells in organisms continue to specialize, developing to a fine degree the properties of living substance. Each emerging specialty is new and yet not new. It reminds one of the creation of a geometry in which a series of new theorems arises from certain given material, basic assumptions. The theorems of life are successful novel forms, and the basic assumptions are the given, built-in potentialities of protoplasm. In a sense, evolution is a spelling-out process.

Cells stretch and contract like springs, shape honeycomb calcium-crystal structures firm as reefs of coral, glow in the dark. The precursors of muscle, shell and bone, luminescent organs. All of them were once queer, off-beat creatures, freaks suffering from inborn defects, the results of inherited copying errors. Unlike legions and legions of other misfit breeds with other defects, they managed to endure. Now things like them find their places in newly formed patterns, in organisms made up of many cells. Specialists are often deficient individuals that thrive in the right communal setting.

There is one further class of specialists which becomes more and more important in the patterning of animate matter. As settled areas or nations grow larger, they develop more efficient methods of communication—smoke signals and beating tom-toms and pony expresses and telegraph and radio and radar and television systems. A rapid flow of information helps bind things together, to make a unified community or society out of scattered individuals.

It is the same with organisms. If a group of cells grew so large that its remotest parts had no efficient way of keeping in touch with one another, it would be a sluggish and poorly co-ordinated mass of protoplasm. In other words, the size

130

of organisms would be severely limited without good communications, so limited, perhaps, that all species would be tiny invisible specks. The coming of bigger and bigger organisms is possible because of specialists that transmit messages.

All cells produce some electricity, since there is a two-way traffic of electrically charged particles in and out of their membranes. But the messenger or nerve cell develops into a full-scale, full-time electrical device. It becomes a kind of self-charging storage battery, and from it extend fibers which carry currents. Nerve cells are in constant touch with the world. They pick up signals which represent the course of outside events, and relay the signals to other nerve cells and various tissues of the organism. They overcome distance and time, as organisms expand into larger and larger organized systems of cells. They play a role of increasing significance as patterns of evolving matter become increasingly complex.

The triumph of organization in at least one small corner of the universe. Life is like a shout of defiance in a desolate place, a challenge to all the forces of chaos everywhere, to all the things that tend to break down patterns as fast as they appear. Cells working together in groups occupy the center of the stage. But there are much smaller units behind the scenes, and it is their activities which produce patterns, including patterns that endure. The life of a star is determined by reactions among atoms fusing at its core. The life of an organism involves the workings of invisible genes in the nuclei of its cells.

The coming of specialists and new organisms depends to a large extent on a steady and concurrent revolution in the shaping of genes. The earliest naked genes may not have been particularly good at making images of themselves. They must have erred frequently. After all, they were new hands at a difficult job, and the quality of image-making has been improving ever since. A single reproducing molecule is in a sense responsible to itself alone. It has a certain amount of leeway in the duplicating process. It may err in a variety of ways and still continue to increase its numbers. Even if it fails to reproduce, it will not affect the survival of other strains of genes.

But requirements are more strict for genes functioning as members of groups. Together they direct the shaping of every specialized structure, light-sensitive "eye" spots and mouths and gullets of individual cells and organisms. Such work calls for a high degree of precision and finesse. This is no longer the undisciplined, haphazard world which gave rise to swarms of naked genes. Existing organisms are products, not of single genes but of gene "constellations"—groups of hundreds or thousands of genes, each of which has its specific job to do and controls its specific chemical reaction and depends on the successful operations of all the other genes in the system.

Genes become specialists and in the process specialized cells are created. Now we have mutually dependent genes, and it is increasingly important that every gene in the constellation reproduce itself accurately. In fact, the whole trend is toward more and more accurate self-duplication. Copying errors, mutations, must be as infrequent as possible. A constellation of a thousand genes is like a fine mechanism of a thousand precisely machined and intermeshed parts. If one part is not made to specifications, the works will jam. If one gene is defective, it can and often does throw the entire organism out of kilter.

Living things tend to maintain themselves with an intensive and overriding persistence. The laws of their existence favor accurate duplication, a low rate of genetic mutation. The tendency toward lower and lower rates implies that ideally they would drop to zero. As we have seen, this would mean the end of evolution because mutation is the essential source of novelty. But evolution defeats the antievolutionary conservatism of every biological system, every biological

132

process. A zero mutation rate, perfect copying, is never attained for one very good reason. Mutations are accidents and accidents will happen.

We do not know how accurately genes reproduced in the beginning. On the other hand, there is good evidence for modern times. Research on many existing species, from bacteria and fruit flies to mice and men, show that they have reached a high level of proficiency today. Of course, some genes are better image-makers than others. But a reasonable figure for the mutation rate of an average gene during the shaping of an individual may be about one in four million.

To put it another way, a typical gene builds an image of itself and the image gene builds another image and so on. The process continues through some four million copyings before a mutant is produced, a gene which differs significantly from its ancestors. In terms of the generation time of higher organisms, the gene may go on reproducing itself faithfully for hundreds of thousands of years. This is an impressive feat when we recall that such self-duplication demands the assembly, time after time, of helical sections of DNA which contain many thousands of base pairs arranged in just the right order.

Mutations are rare, but favorable mutations are rarer still. Even by the most generous estimates, the odds are that no more than one out of every thousand mutations will turn out to be a positive advantage for the organism. In other words, during the history of a single gene mutating at a representative rate, a favorable change may come up once in every four billion copyings, a rather low batting average. Of course, the more genes an organism has, the greater the chances of a mutation of any sort occurring in any given generation. Still, good genes are few and far between. Although opportunity knocks more than once in the course of evolution, it may be a long, long time between visits. Judging by the records, nature is not always interested in getting places fast.

133

A science-fiction example, a theoretical process in a theoretical universe, indicates how things actually evolve. Assume that we set about breeding a higher animal, beginning practically from scratch with a simple organism. The point of this game is to wait for favorable mutations and let them accumulate so that their effects add up, producing more and more complex creatures. Assume also that conditions are right, that there is space and food and time enough for every mutant strain to survive and yield offspring. (We shall soon discover that this is a very big assumption indeed.)

To start, we let the simple organism multiply until it produces a thousand different varieties of itself, that is, a thousand strains each having a different mutation. We need a thousand varieties, because on the average only one out of a thousand mutations will be favorable. In other words, we need a thousand varieties to get one improved strain, say, an organism which is faster or stronger than its relatives. It is a blue-ribbon variety, a prize winner with a small but distinct superiority.

The next step calls for a somewhat more advanced strain with not one but two favorable genes. So each of the thousand varieties, including the prize winner, produces a thousand more varieties or mutants—which makes a grand total of a million. It is the prize winner variety, of course, that yields the one-in-a-million strain with two favorable mutations.

Before burying ourselves in astronomical numbers, it might be well to summarize where we stand so far. To obtain one favorable mutation we needed a thousand varieties of organisms. Two favorable mutations called for 1000^2 varieties, that is, a thousand raised to the second power or 1000 times 1000. Looking ahead, three favorable mutations would require 1000^3 varieties (a thousand raised to the third power, or 1000 times 1000 times 1000, which is a billion), four favorable mutations would require 1000^4 or a thousand billion varieties, and so on. To compute how many strains would be needed to yield an organism with a specified number of favorable mutations, you multiply a thousand by itself that number of times.

The arithmetic of our example and the arithmetic of gambling are the same. It is like playing with a roulette wheel that has a thousand different numbers. In such a game it would take a thousand spins, on the average, for any given number to turn up, and you place your bets accordingly. If the bank were content merely with breaking even, it would give you odds of a thousand to one. If you are very rich and decide to bet on the possibility of any two chosen numbers turning up one after the other on two successive spins, the odds multiply and become a million to one. Betting on a run of three numbers, say 6 and 73 and 927, sends the odds soaring to a billion to one. The odds build up similarly in our hypothetical way of developing living forms.

How many favorable mutations must we accumulate, to go from a simple organism to a tiger or an elephant or a man? As a sheer guess, but again keeping our estimates very much on the conservative side, let us take the good round number of a million. Although this number could easily be ten or a hundred times greater, it is adequate to illustrate our point. To obtain a million step-by-step improvements, mutations leading to the enormously refined sets of genes that shape higher animals, would require $1000^{1,000,000}$ different strains in all—one thousand raised to the millionth power, or one thousand multiplied by itself a million times.

This number is not infinity, but it might as well be. Simply to print it out digit by digit, one followed by three million zeros, would require a book thicker than *From Here to Eternity*. Imagine a Noah's Ark containing just one representative of every mutant strain which must have existed to arrive at an advanced modern species. The entire observable universe, a sphere more than three billion light-years in radius, is not nearly big enough to hold such an ark. It would be far too small even if each strain were no larger than an atom. Furthermore, time is not long enough for all that breeding. Suppose that a billion strains came into being every second. That is still not nearly fast enough to yield $1000^{1,000,000}$ varieties in a thousand billion years or a thousand billion billion years.

This is where our theoretical example breaks down completely. Neither time nor space is available for us to get anywhere by letting all strains keep multiplying until they produce favorable mutations. On that basis the living earth would have long since ended as an overcrowded, clogged-up mass of dead and dying protoplasm, and things might never have gone as far as a single cell. In a world where simply existing involves continual adjustment and readjustment—continual change—not mutating is generally equivalent to extinction.

Nature leans heavily on random mutation, but random mutation alone is not enough. If it were all a gamble pure and simple, a great roulette game in which you wait until the laws of chance bring your numbers up, evolution could not take place. Evolution is a ceaseless interplay between mutation and something else. Biologists call it natural selection. The fundamental fact is that all strains of organisms do not survive. The vast majority of them are nipped in the bud.

Here is the sort of thing that happened long ago and is still happening. Here is a simple organism, a form shaped largely by the activities of its set or constellation of genes. It seeks food and swims along with the aid of whiplike tendrils, threads of protein. It resembles all similar organisms, except for one small and significant difference.

Something blind and purposeless has occurred at the molecular level. Out of the hundreds of genes which our swimmer inherited, one of the genes concerned with biochemical reactions required to produce tendrils has mutated. There has been a copying error involving one pair of bases in one section of one DNA helix, a flaw in a part of an intricately coiled pattern of atoms. This change leads to the formation of tendrils which are a bit longer or thicker or more mobile than the run-of-the-mill variety.

So the organism moves through the water a bit faster. The result is that, operating on the familiar principle that the early bird catches the worm, it will tend to get at food a bit sooner than its unmutated brethren. It need not arrive a great deal sooner. A very small advantage may be all that is necessary.

Suppose that similar organisms without the favorable mutation give rise to a thousand offspring. Suppose further that the faster organism eats sufficiently better to reproduce somewhat more successfully and gives rise to a single extra offspring. That is, it outmultiplies its fellows by 1001 to 1000. There is only one more reproducing unit in the population having the favorable mutation. The difference is hardly spectacular at this point.

But it is more than enough in the long run. The advantage builds up generation after generation. Some two thousand or so generations later the situation has altered markedly. The faster organism was once a minority of one. Now its descendants are about ten times more numerous than those of the slower organisms—and this is a spectacular difference. Two thousand generations may be only twenty-five years for a simple organism, and it will not be long before the slower breeds are swamped. They will lose out entirely, leaving the way clear for the continuing evolution of favorably equipped strains.

The same laws of natural selection apply to the shaping of all forms throughout the ages. In such a process there is no need to find living space for enormous masses of protoplasm. There is no need to depend solely on gambling, on the odds of the house. Nature beats the odds, and keeps beating the odds over and over again. Mutations arise purely by chance, but they do not arise in a pure-chance world, a world of chaos. They take their places in a world already bustling with patterns. They take their places in one of the inherited patterns that produce living things, in one of the constellations of smoothly interacting genes. The rule from then on is sink or swim.

If the newcomer can fit into a gene constellation, if it can earn its keep by making some positive contribution to the organism's way of life, it will survive and spread. If not, it is eliminated together with the strain it helped shape. The penalty is extinction. The less fit and the unfit are simply wiped off the face of the earth. Evolution proceeds to generate increasingly complex patterns by the selection of appropriate freaks.

Mutation and selection are sufficient for the steady emergence of new forms. But one phenomenon, sex, helps speed evolution considerably. If organisms developed solely by the accumulation of favorable mutations in the independent organisms of separate strains, things would move at a snail's pace. Sex permits the continual sharing and mixing of hereditary materials. From a fundamental biological standpoint it is primarily a way of increasing the odds, a way of reshuffling genes, of producing a wider variety of permutations and combinations among sections of DNA molecules. By bringing large numbers of mutations together, sex makes it possible to generate novelty much faster than would otherwise be the case.

Evolution by unmating strains only would be comparable to an inefficient educational system. Suppose that every science student were trained by a private tutor and never allowed to participate in a class or discuss his problems with other investigators. Under such a setup new knowledge would probably come, but very slowly. Students might make brilliant discoveries in relative isolation. But they would stand a good chance of "discovering" things which others had already found before them. There would be a tendency to go over the same ground again and again, to duplicate errors and dead-end studies. The sharing of ideas and experiences in the actual educational system corresponds to cross-fertilization and the sharing of genes in evolution. The process is fruitful in both areas.

Sex appears early in the history of life. It has even been observed in bacteria. Two bacteria meet and make contact and within a few minutes a long chain of DNA begins passing from one bacterium, the male, into the body of the female. The union may last for half an hour or so. Then the pair separates, and the female divides, to yield two offspring which contain a combination of hereditary materials from both parents.

Apparently this type of microscopic breeding is a rare event. Sex does not seem to be important in the lives of most bacteria. Perhaps only one strain in a million has male and female members. But the possibility of sex in such primitive organisms, a relatively recent discovery, indicates that nature may have been experimenting with the process not long after the coming of the first cells. As a result, life is much further along than it would be in a sexless world.

A sexless world would be a lazy, slow-motion world. Evolution would proceed at least a thousand times more sluggishly. There would be no many-celled organisms on our earth today. The seas would contain only primitive single cells, if life had evolved even that far. Moreover, the future would not bring notable progress. When the sun began petering out, the highest forms of life would still probably be microscopic groups of cells. The land would be barren and would never have trees or flowers or animals that live in the open air. In a sexless world, evolution ceases before it has a chance to become interesting.

Sex provides the spark, the extra push, the acceleration which permits the coming of advanced organisms long before the sun sinks into senility. So life as represented by ourselves and our descendants, human or otherwise, has ample time to evolve further and perhaps to find more suitable homelands elsewhere in the Milky Way.

But opportunity has always been extremely expensive in terms of the individual. A certain ruthlessness underlies evolution, a ruthlessness so intensive that it is difficult to grasp. Think of the laboratory experiment in which bacteria are exposed to a change of environment, to new conditions represented by the presence of an antibiotic drug. Death sweeps terribly through the population. The Black Plague was mild and merciful in comparison with this mass dying. A billion organisms; 999,999,997 killed. Almost perfect annihilation.

Now think of nature's experiments, of similar annihilations among all living things—of all possible causes and agencies, not just a contaminated environment. The spread of sucking parasites, the coming of ice ages and droughts, the turning of fruitful lands into deserts, the uplifting and sinking of continental shelves, and floods, eruptions, competitors invading, food shortages. Creatures that have attained a well-adjusted way of life, a measure of equilibrium in the shifting scheme of things, being surpassed by better-adjusted mutants. Series of emergencies of all sorts developing through eons, for more than two billion years.

Multitudes burst into being every generation, rising like a great surge of surf. Every generation is a universe of organisms having strange unlikely forms, like insects magnified many times or things with eyes on luminescent stalks hauled up from the depths of the ocean. A universe of organisms and most of them failures. Most of them cut down. Another generation, the forward roll of another wave, another cutting-down. And so on and on starting from the earliest times of life, and even earlier among hordes of molecules which were perhaps not alive but which reproduced. Most of yesterday's creatures are dead-end experiments, stuff in the backroom discarded for the junkman.

Every species that exists and thrives today, every species that exists and thrives at any time, has gone through hell. The death rate at every stage has been terrific. Every species is a residue of vanished legions, an infinitesimal fraction of all the living things that have passed forever, the latest of a long, long line of cruder and extinct models. We are justifiably impressed with our kind and the forms we know, with intricately patterned living things. The human brain, the eye of a hawk which detects a mouse clearly from a height of more than five hundred feet, a seed that somehow takes roots and fights for life and becomes a twisted tree high in the dry crack of a ruined temple wall.

Such things are wonders and challenges. It is sometimes difficult to believe that they arose slowly over the ages from the accumulation and weeding out and mixing of mutations. But we see so little compared to what has gone before. It is as if a person without any previous knowledge about gods or places of worship came for the first time upon a cathedral in full splendor. He is ignorant of the places of underground darkness where cave men practiced burial rites, overgrown jungle crypts containing ancestral remains in painted urns, pyramids and Stonehenges and the faces on Easter Island, temples made of wood, temples of hardened mud, temples of gold and marble. Not knowing all this and more, our observer might not be able to account for a cathedral.

We tend to see every plant and animal as if it arose full-blown without a past, without a history. We may at times forget the vast numbers of in-between and transitional forms which preceded it. If by some miracle all the creatures that ever existed appeared before us in a panorama on a wide plain, we could appreciate more fully the step-by-step nature of origins.

But the wonder would remain. Wonder never dies with growing knowledge. It is renewed and replenished. We do not think less of living creatures, or less of cathedrals, because they have evolved from simpler things. Our curiosity is heightened. We explore the past in more places and, step by step, learn more about a process that moves irresistibly on beyond cells and simple organizations of cells.

The Last Half-
Billion Years
9

HALF a billion years to go. The seas are well stocked now.
Bacteria, amebas and other single-cell creatures are most
abundant, as they will always be. There are also sponges,
sand-burrowing worms, corals whose skeletons grow into
great jagged reefs. Bulbous sea anemones fasten themselves
to rocks, living off what the tides and waves bring. Jellyfish
with pulsing mantles half-drift and half-swim; crablike things
may scuttle across the bottom. These and a host of other organisms seem a long way from man or from apes. So much
is yet to come, so many forms which are nowhere to be
found among relatively simple marine creatures.

But it all depends on what time scale you use. A millennium
is nothing at all in the career of a star; twenty minutes is an
entire lifetime for some bacteria. Our time scale is based on
the process of pattern-forming from the beginning, before the
Milky Way existed. More than nine billion years ago there

was only a single "species," atoms of hydrogen in the original unshaped cloud. Four or five billion years ago the earth jelled out of gases left over from the building of the sun. At least two or three billion years ago the first cells came into being. These are really big events in cosmic history, revolutions and Magna Cartas and Declarations of Independence. They are properly measured in units of a billion years.

From here on, until man appears, the shaping of matter includes somewhat lesser events measured in smaller units. A great deal will happen, but in a sense it represents the spelling out of established principles. The basic biochemical reactions of all creatures to come do not differ radically from those of single cells. Most of the same kinds of enzymes are at work, and the same sort of genes, and the same processes of mutation and natural selection.

We have already traveled most of the way, and our own yesterdays are very close. We are on the last lap, having completed ninety-five percent of the trip from the original cloud. This is roughly equivalent to arriving at a point 120 miles from New York on an airline flight that started in San Francisco.

Half a billion years in the future there will be men, and evolution will be off on a new tack. Right now, one of the most advanced primeval creatures is the sea squirt. This living sack looks something like a tomato and is just about as adventuresome. It clings to a rock, using rhythmically moving hairs or cilia to sweep water into its sack. Bacteria and other foods are caught in a sticky "flypaper" substance lining the inner walls. Then the used water is squirted away through a waste-disposal spout.

If evolution goes chiefly along these lines, life will not be very interesting. But it by-passes the squatters, at least the adults of the species. The young are not by-passed. The future belongs to them, because they get around more. The larvae of the sea squirt are shaped like tadpoles and have long

144

propelling tails. They wriggle up toward the surface where there is light. Most of them die. The rest swim back, fasten to rocks, and grow into staid and unexploring adults. Their heyday of movement has lasted only a day or two. Among conventional law-abiding sea squirts, the young always come home to roost.

But some larvae, or forms like permanent larvae do not conform to ancestral patterns of behavior. They are freaks, "retarded" organisms by the standards of the times, carrying mutated genes which inhibit or delay normal growth processes. The end of the active, free-swimming stage comes later, or never comes at all. Perhaps some larvae explore for longer and longer periods before returning to permanent places on rocks. Eventually forms appear which do not stop swimming and do not return. They are juvenile delinquents by traditional standards, or, from another point of view, possessors of prolonged youth. They retain their mobility and do not become the old-fashioned type of adult. In a sense they die without ever growing up.

Tossed into the pool of life, these tiny swimmers become raw material for the building of a long series of new patterns. They have one feature of special interest. Running along almost the entire length of their tails is a slender rod made of tough elastic cartilage. It is an aid to efficient swimming, a stiffening element like the strips of celluloid that may be inserted into the edges of shirt collars. The rod is the first sign of what will become a backbone in more advanced forms. The larvae of sedentary stay-at-homes will develop into swift marine creatures with spiky fins and jaws and teeth for killing.

Two hundred million years pass and fish dominate the seas. No animals have left the seas yet, but their food has preceded them. The land is no longer a place of naked mountains and cliffs and broken boulders and pebbles and sands. Plants have moved out of the waters and spread to what was

145

once a barren crust. There are tropical storms and dense tropical rain forests. This wilderness is ripe for settlers. The pioneers may come in swampy waters, or in mud pools along river banks covered by seasonal flooding.

Now, things are upset and stirring. Fish in the basins of the seas, in the big waters, live as they have always lived. But at the edges, in inland waters and perhaps near coasts and shores, the pressure builds up. There are creatures which have air bladders and can take air in gulps. Perhaps they breed so successfully that conditions become overcrowded. Perhaps they need more living space and more food, which local waters no longer provide.

Some of the air gulpers have strong fins or flippers and can flop along on land for short distances and reach unstocked ponds. Insects may exist there, and early versions of spiders and scorpions and mites. If so, crawling fish find food. Some of them may overdo it, going too far in their search, past the point of no return. They rot or the sun bakes them. Creatures which can travel furthest and withstand drying out, and either come back alive or find new waters, have wider zones to hunt in, and eat better. They always return to water, like night prowlers to caves, for the link with the seas is not yet broken. But they are favored in another phase of the weeding-out process.

Nature dips deep into her bag of mutations, and tries one after the other. All possibilities are explored; every mutation has its chance. New genes face highly competitive tests. The genes of a particularly well-adapted fish represent an established combination, and fitting into the combination may not be easy. In overcrowded times, as in every crisis, favorable mutations are at an extra-high premium. Conditions are demanding. The genes of some fish happen to produce skins that dry somewhat less rapidly in the sun, or more efficient ways of holding water in the tissues, or refined air bladders a bit closer to lungs.

146

THE COMPLEXITY OF A CELL

if a single cell were magnified a million times, it would look something like this ▶

nucleus

ME SIMPLE PATTERNS OF LIFE

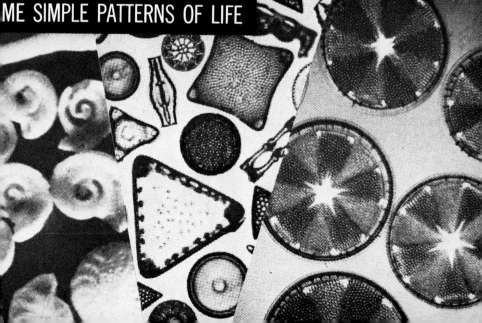

SOME HIGHLIGHTS OF THE LAST HALF BILLION YEARS

65 million years ago ... *First "pre-monkeys"*

165 million years ago ... *First birds and mammals*

205 million years ago ... *First dinosaurs*

325 million years ago ... *First amphibians*

425 million years ago ... *Earliest known fishes*

simple organisms

Other genes give rise to larger and stronger flippers with gripping elements at the ends, the precursors of claws and toes and fingers, and it is possible to move greater distances. Even the smallest improvements pay off in terms of survival and self-perpetuation. The process is slow. Fishlike things flop and flounder about for ages in muddy places before the coming of early amphibians, the ancestors of salamanders and frogs.

We move further along, another seventy-five million years or so. There is not much time left. We have already traveled more than half of that last lap. Now the long and difficult step from sea to land is completed. The pioneers arrive in full force. Animals that can live out of water, inherit the earth. They have evolved from ancient in-between species—squat creatures resembling lizards, about two feet long from snout to tail, living chiefly on insects.

Reptiles represent a new direction, a new branching out. But one feature of this process follows an old precedent in the evolution of matter. From the very beginning things have tended to grow bigger and bigger. The synthesis of chemical elements in stars starts with protons and builds up to atomic patterns like uranium, which includes 238 protons. As far as the familiar elements of nature are concerned, however, that appears to be coming fairly close to the limit. Systems are unstable if they are much heavier than that.

Reproducing molecules and cells also grow and reach limits. One of the limits comes during the age of reptiles. Small creatures which run about nimbly on their hind legs are forerunners of a menagerie of forms at least as fantastic as unicorns and griffins. Dinosaurs are science fiction come to life, armored destroyers and dreadnoughts of the land. The smallest are about the size of cats. The largest include Brontosaurus, the long-necked "thunder reptile" pictured in most textbooks, and other forms which must have weighed nearly fifty tons.

147

There are duck-billed dinosaurs, and dinosaurs that look something like a cross between a beaver and a turtle. Triceratops resembles a rhinoceros with three sharp horns, a short one at the end of its nose and long ones above each eye. Stegosaurus has a spiked tail and two rows of plates along its back. Perhaps the most ferocious of all is Tyrannosaurus, which walks on two feet, kills with the aid of saber teeth and may be twenty feet high. Tyrannosaurus also happens to be a kind of culmination of viciousness, one of the last of the line. Some time after reaching their prime, giant reptiles begin to dwindle and eventually disappear. But they managed to survive eighty million years or more.

The passing of the dinosaurs is still a mystery. One theory suggests that there was a long hot spell. The land dried up and mountains erupted and the giant reptiles died under sizzling, treacherous conditions. This is the popular Hollywood version. Animated cartoons in Technicolor show the last dinosaurs staggering along in a Death Valley desert with their tongues hanging out. The sun beats down on their backs and volcanoes spout red-hot lava in the background. The end finds them roaring with panic as they sink into mud pits and quicksands, or falling to the sand in dead faints.

Most people in science wince at such melodrama. Not that we know these things never occurred. They might have developed that way. But the literalness of presentation, the pile-up of detail, gives a false impression of knowledge where we do not know. The dinosaurs may have succumbed to some epidemic, and there are other theories. The Hollywood heat-death cliché creates an illusion of certainty, finality. Everything is there, everything except doubt. The only element that has been eliminated is the most essential element of all—the nature of learning, the facing of problems and possibilities as they arise like new forms in evolution itself. In missing this, all the melodramas succeed in distorting utterly the spirit of research.

148

The dying out of dinosaurs brings us to a relative lull, a period of letdown and anticlimax. Something mighty has fallen. This is another one of the many evolutionary events that are really preludes to more fruitful times but seem like endings. The places where the dinosaurs were are quieter now, especially quiet for certain rat-sized creatures that lived in the shadow of the monsters—and made sure to get out of the way when the monsters came by like heavy trucks on the center passing lane of a three-lane highway. Although an observer might never guess it, the descendants of these puny animals will take the dinosaurs' place as lords of creation.

Meanwhile there is a biological vacuum, a niche waiting to be filled. And it will be filled. Sooner or later life comes flooding into every available territory. But first, a long pause in evolution. The pause lasts millions of years. The little scurrying creatures do not develop in a hurry. It is as if they are mobilizing their forces. Perhaps it is a time of adjustment. The dinosaurs were masters of living things, but slaves of the environment. They were cold-blooded, like fish and amphibians and smaller surviving reptiles. The temperature of their bodies depended on the temperature of the outside world. It varied as a thermometer varies. The dinosaurs were great half-robots that operated efficiently when the weather was right, but sputtered and slowed to a halt under extreme conditions of heat or cold.

The creatures that will replace dinosaurs are rather less like robots. They can adjust and, by adjusting, endure wider variations. They carry their own climate around with them. They are warm-blooded, which means that their body temperatures tend to remain steady despite changes outside. Their weather is enveloped, contained, built in. They are like rooms equipped with thermostats which adjust furnaces as the weather changes and manage to keep internal temperatures at a fairly even keel.

Looking at things another way, successful gene constellations are in the process of evolving. Coiled DNA molecules, remote descendants of early reproducing particles, are achieving more stable environments for themselves. Naked genes long ago built nuclear membranes around themselves and cell walls around nuclei, installing themselves inside double capsules. Later genes built cells specialized for further protection, scales and armor and skin and horns and teeth. Now they take another important step. They evolve a stable internal climate for the cells which enclose them. Reproducing molecules continue to prosper inside the more and more complex shells which are evolving organisms.

The new patterns, the new varieties of gene-enclosing shells, are mammals with warm blood. More than seventy-five million years have passed since they first appeared on earth. They have had to bide their time. Now, after the pause, they begin to spread and give rise to many different forms—to the forerunners of modern species like sheep and lions and elephants and whales and monkeys and apes and men. Now we have come about 470,000,000 years from the days of the sea-squirt larvae. In terms of a flight from San Francisco to New York, we are tightening our seat belts and only a few minutes out of La Guardia Airport.

The journey has been an eventful one. Starting with single cells, animate matter has organized itself into supercommunities of cells, creatures made up of thousands of billions of living units. The units have been organized into tissues and organs, subpatterns with large frameworks. All these subpatterns evolved together. But one of them has been selected for the unfolding of fresh possibilities. The communicating system, the brain, has played an outstanding part in the evolution of complex organisms.

Looking back, we see in procession the drama of one kind of evolving stuff. Nerve cells, electrical elements which trans-

150

mit and receive signals, grew the way vines grow. They extended fibers and the tips of the fibers met the growing fibers of other nerve cells—the delicate touching of threads of protoplasm, the forming of electrical circuits in living things.

Back to the squatters and drifters, sea anemones and jellyfish and other soft-bodied creatures. No brains yet. But in some species nerve nets appeared, loose lacings of fibers which permitted crude convulsive movements. Touch a sea anemone anywhere and it contracts all over, and it always responds in the same way.

Then came the crawlers and the swimmers and more refined responses. A significant change took place among creatures rapidly on the move. Another condensing process, a concentration of nerve tissue in compact and more elaborate circuits. Main nerves, throughways and busy channels of communication, gathered into a cable running along the spine. Headquarters were located up front at the prow end of the organism, the eye-nose-and-ear end which makes first contact with prey and enemies. The spinal cord bulged up front into a kind of benign tumor. It filled the chamber of the skull, forming the brain.

The brain became a place where signals are focused like the sun's rays brought to a hot, intense spot by a magnifying lens. An intricate system of relays interposed between sensation and action, an organ for the endless interplay of messages. Hunger, the urge to kill, spawning time—unrest in the organism produced signals, channeled irritations, to the brain. Danger, shifting currents, waves of light and sound under water—changes in the environment produced other signals, also conducted to the brain. The brain, buzzing and alive with signals, did what it could to make the best of both worlds. It transmitted action signals or orders to muscles, to tail and fins, and received answering signals indicating how the orders were obeyed. And more signals flowed to the

151

muscles and more answers came back in a round of continual adjustments and readjustments which were migrations, conquests, escapes.

Descendants of fish left the seas. The brain was exposed to the irritations and goadings and challenges of a new environment, to a barrage of sense impressions of a more varied sort, a flood of new signals. The nerve-tumor grew. The highest center, the cerebrum or cerebral hemispheres, grew most of all and buried more primitive structures under a mass of smooth white nerve tissue. And then a dark "stain" appeared on the smooth surface, a tiny bit of gray matter, like a parasitic mold. An extra patch of specialized nerve tissue, evolved perhaps in high-pressure times of land invasions, may have arisen among early amphibious things resembling frogs.

The patch came last of all centers, and the spaces inside the skull were already crowded. It spread like a gray tide over the white hemispheres and spilled down into the fissures and clefts between. Forcing its way everywhere, it grew into a many-folded convoluted sheet, the cortex or outer bark. The cortex, shaped by natural selection through countless generations of reptiles and mammals, represents the most complex and advanced center of the brain. With it have come new capacities of memory, learning, planning, imagination. In our story it has now reached its highest development in the predecessors of monkeys, apes and men.

Life on the march. These creatures have evolved swiftly from simple organisms, considering the span of time that has elapsed since the beginning of stars and galaxies. Five hundred million years is not so much compared with nine and a half billion years. But within the framework of life, rates of evolution may vary widely. It is like what takes place underground as a tree grows. The tree sinks its roots deep and in many directions, groping for water in the dark. Some roots find the going difficult. They burrow slowly in hard ground, faster where the soil is looser, and perhaps slowly again further on. Or they meet obstacles and must grow at angles and twist past buried boulders and creep up through granite cracks.

Other roots move more steadily for a time and throw out many branches. The branches throw out smaller branches. But eventually sources of water dwindle away, and most of the branches shrivel. Still other roots strike it rich, and there are boom times. Their branches are numerous and grow at a faster pace and keep digging deeper for more and more water. Evolution is also a system of many roots and branches, of the withering away and extinction of species and varieties, of booming interludes of growth. It also depends on what the environment happens to offer and on available reserves of mutations. And it moves fastest where opportunities happen to be richest.

Biological conservatism, the difficulty of finding genes that fit into established gene constellations, sees to it that evolution usually makes haste slowly. Good fossil records for the horse indicate how the process works. Eohippus, the dawn horse, lived about sixty million years ago. It was no larger than a collie dog. It roamed about in dense tropical and temperate-zone forests, living off soft buds and leaves which it chopped up with short chunky teeth.

Later, in cooler and drier times, some of the descendants of Eohippus changed their eating habits. Forests were becoming sparser and in many regions gradually gave way to widespread open places, steppes and prairies—where extremely tough plants grew, grasses with fibers supported by a gritty glasslike substance. Horses began making the shift from browsing to grazing. They had to grind grasses growing in sandy soils, and under such conditions short teeth wear away quickly. In other words, out of a large population those horses which happened to have longer-than-average teeth were at a distinct advantage. They ate longer and lived longer than their less fortunate contemporaries. The difference at first may have amounted to only a year of extra grazing, or perhaps only a few months, but still, that meant more time to produce more offspring.

Nature has been in no hurry to evolve Equus, the modern horse, from Eohippus. Tooth lengths increased from a third of an inch or so to more than an inch and a half in sixty million years, or about a fiftieth of an inch for every ten thousand centuries. Of course, this is only an average figure. Growth rates varied considerably during that period. And all along there were other changes. Horses became bigger, longer-limbed, faster. Eohippus had fourteen toes (four on each front leg and three on each hind leg) and fourteen little hooves, one on each toe. Feet with single hooves are a recent development.

Furthermore, new varieties did not come one after the other in a neat logical series. Nature follows no script. She ad-libs and improvises. The history of horses is a record of trial and error and many strange experiments, like the history of all living things—or the history of the man-made things that are replacing horses. Imagine a complete collection of all models of automobiles, vintage to modern. Hundreds of cars are exhibited, roughly in the order of their appearance. The first cars borrow most heavily from the past. They are modified carriages.

Innovations often exist together with old and surprisingly crude features. Here is one early model with a relatively sophisticated transmission system, and yet we see that it bumped along on solid rubber tires. Another model has good headlights and a promising self-starter. But its chassis looks Victorian. A section devoted to streamlined cars shows that improvements may go out of style for a time and come into their own later. These models were not successful when they were introduced—times were not yet ripe. But they ultimately caught on and spread over the nation's highways.

154

Other displays demonstrate forcibly that most changes are minor ones which merely stimulate the buying of new cars and hasten the obsolescence of last year's models.

Such an exhibit would be extremely confusing to most of us. So the usual practice for simplicity's sake is to show a few models indicating the transition from high, tinny pioneers built along horse-and-buggy lines to today's low-slung monsters. Similarly, in describing an evolutionary line biologists may present a few types to illustrate general trends. But the shaping of species is far more complicated and devious than the development of automobiles. Major changes are infrequent, and between major changes we may have a legion of minor alterations which improve the "market value" of the product. At least fifteen million generations, at least 1,500,-000,000,000 individual horses and thousands upon thousands of mutations, were involved in the route from Eohippus to Equus.

The evolution of all higher animals proceeds in this way. A species is a population of organisms which have one basic thing in common, a "pool" of thousands of genes. In other words, every species has its characteristic set of genes. The genes flow continually through the group as they are shuffled and reshuffled by interbreeding. As long as the group remains together, living in the same territory and moving freely within that territory, it tends to keep its distinctive hereditary features.

But a species may split into two or more populations, and the splitting may be a first step in the formation of new species. Some twenty to thirty million years ago a new group of volcanic islands, the Galápagos, was thrust up above the surface of the Pacific Ocean about six hundred miles from the nearest land. Masses of ashes and lava arose, as lifeless as the earth itself before the coming of cells. But life invaded islands, as it invades all places, and each invasion is a kind of splitting-off. The pioneers left their homelands.

The earliest invaders were presumably simple mosses and plants which can grow in the most desolate places. Winds and ocean currents carried their seeds from the mainland to the new shores. Higher organisms arrived later. Among them was a flock of finches, or perhaps only a single pair. Blown out to sea, the sparrowlike birds found a home on the islands. They lived near the ground, and their diet consisted mainly of seeds.

The ancestors of these birds have developed along many different lines, into new patterns of form and behavior. They differ in size and, most radically, in the shapes of their beaks, which have become specialized for eating cactus, fruits, insects and other available foods. Most remarkable of all is a unique "woodpecker" finch, a tree climber and tool user. It drills holes through bark, picks up a twig or snaps off a handy cactus thorn, and uses it to pry out insects. At least fourteen species of finches exist on the Galápagos, all of them descended from the first settlers. They are known as "Darwin's finches," because they played an important role in shaping the great naturalist's ideas about the origin of species.

Isolation need not be as complete or clear-cut as life on an island. The original population and its enterprising emigrants may be separated by mountains or great prairies between forests or intervening lakes and canyons. Isolation favors increasing dissimilarities among separate populations, until resemblances may be difficult to detect and productive interbreeding is no longer possible. And, more often than not, the longer the isolation the greater the differences.

The situation may be compared to what happens when you revisit your home town after longer and longer absences. If you are young and have been away only a few years, things may not have changed much. Streets and houses look the way they looked when you left. The places where you played as a child are still the same and so are most of the

156

friends you played with. The differences in your town and in you are much greater twenty-five years later. Many of the old homes and stores have been torn down. New houses stand where there were once woods and open fields. Your friends have changed. There are many newcomers in town now, and you recognize hardly any of the children and young people. You are more of a stranger, a Rip Van Winkle returned. Imagine how different things would be and how differently you would feel if you could revisit your home town a hundred generations later.

Time and evolution bring about much more radical changes. An isolated population may be small at the beginning, with relatively few breeding organisms. Its very smallness favors variety, just as a small class favors variety and individuality of expression among students. There is a kind of "loosening up" in the closely integrated system that is a gene pool. Things are more flexible, readier for change, and certain genes have a greater chance to express themselves and exert their effects than they would in bigger populations.

Mutations are not lost or buried so rapidly among small groups. It is something like a time of crisis in a political system, when the nation is in a state of confusion and traditional forms are no longer sufficient and new ideas may take root. It is a most favorable time for the activities of unusual, off-beat genes and for the emergence of new patterns.

In cases like that of the Galápagos finches, new species are born. But novelty is often achieved at a sacrifice. Such species tend to be rigid as far as meeting emergencies is concerned. Having adapted to local conditions, they may become less plastic and fail to adapt to later changes. A shift in climate or the coming of a competing species may be enough to wipe them out. Mainland birds are generally better at adapting. Island birds are extra-vulnerable to extinction. In fact, judg-

157

ing by what has happened during recent times, island birds are about fifty times more likely to become extinct than mainlanders.

Rare exceptions occur, however, and they may be extremely significant in the history of life. Suppose that a small isolated population has developed a unique genetic capacity for change under suitable conditions. Suppose further that some of its members now end their isolation by entering a new zone, a niche that has not been filled completely. Then evolution may move more rapidly than usual. Basically new forms may arise and spread within a million or a few million years, and compared with customary rates, that is a full-fledged evolutionary "explosion." Such events may be involved in the transition from one major class of animals to another, say, from reptiles to birds.

More than a hundred and fifty million years ago there were reptile-birds, in-between things with feathers and scales and teeth and sharp snouts that had not yet developed into beaks. The feathers grew mainly on their front legs and long tails. According to one theory, they lived in trees and ran and jumped and perhaps glided during their longer leaps. Fossil records are not complete enough to indicate the details of this transition, but some investigators believe that the major steps occurred in a few million years. If so, they may have been the results of changes taking place among the gene pools of small isolated populations, among creatures resembling lizards, with wings which were once feet and, before that, fins.

Creatures that fly, creatures that stalk their prey silent as shadows and then pounce, creatures with horns and tusks and venoms, small swift creatures that dodge and feint and feint again and are off in a split-second escape—life has come a long way from single cells. Life, at this stage of our story, is still a long way from man. A long way in development, but not a long way in time. We are already within shouting dis-

158

tance of the twentieth century and its dominant breeds and its dilemmas.

We are on the verge of something entirely new, a new horizon in the evolution of matter from galactic clouds, not just a new sequence of related species. A new living pattern is imminent. It will differ as widely from other living things as the earliest cells differed from the crystal stuff of rocks. The pattern will be man, the first of a new series of beginnings.

MAN

Forerunners

of Man

10

OUR past is a moment ago, a recent change of subject in a conversation that started at midnight and has many midnights to go. We take the whole span from original cloud to us, the whole ten billion years, and reduce it to one day. On that time scale the day begins at midnight in the cloud. The Milky Way arose a minute or so after seven o'clock in the morning. The sun came exactly on the dot of high noon, the earth at twelve seconds past one, life at twilight, six P.M. It is now four minutes and twelve seconds before midnight, or, on another time scale, about 30,000,000 B.C.

The earth just before the coming of man, just before the second midnight, has not stopped evolving. In places it is in a state of tension, stretched to the breaking point, splitting at the seams. The crust has many gashes. Two great parallel fissures have opened up in Africa, chasms whose walls fall away through dust and smoke deep down to the very base of the continent. Later the land between the fissures sinks to form the great African Rift Valley, the Red Sea filling part of the valley and the River Jordan flowing through another part.

The crust buckles up. The folds complete the building of Alps and Himalayas and Andes and Rockies. And at many points, out of fissures and craters and vents, and out of cracks in the floor of the ocean, moves a thick, smoldering ooze. A sulfurous paste squeezed out of subterranean tubes. White-hot basalt lava, hundreds of thousands of cubic miles of it, rolls down the slopes of volcanoes in France and northern Italy in Alpine regions—and along the Pacific and east of the Rockies.

The earth is bleeding from a thousand wounds. It is restless and heaving throughout the period that includes the gradual emergence of man. We and our predecessors have never known "normal" climates, the conditions that prevailed for about ninety-nine percent of geological time. All modern mammals, from cats and wolves to camels and elephants and giraffes, have developed under similiar conditions along with us. Our kind appears in unsettled times.

Thirty million years ago, at an isolated crossroads in evolution, among innumerable roads which wind and crisscross and merge beyond the horizon. A spreading system of turnpikes and highways and obscure country lanes, a river-delta complex of branches and branches of branches. Somehow, without observing the entrance, we have wandered into the midst of a maze.

We look back along the road in the direction we came from, and the road dips down and away into mists. Somewhere among the branchings of the past at about the time of Eohippus there were prosimians, pre-monkeys. Some of them are already fossils, or fossils-to-be, buried together with the forests they lived in on Rocky Mountain slopes. Some of them survive. They resemble lemurs—"spirits of the dead"— things the size of cats with wide, luminous owl-eyes, living in trees and hunting by night and moving in sudden leaps. Behind us where we cannot see, and extending off to one side, is the beginning of a road which will lead to modern-style monkeys.

But not all prosimians went that way. Here at the crossroads are creatures that have not yet committed themselves; not yet jelled into a living pattern. Creatures like monkeys, but not monkeys, climb trees on all fours. They can swing from branch to branch, but only on a part-time amateur basis. They have not yet developed hands typical of full-fledged swingers. They will travel in two general directions. We look ahead along the crossroads. If we followed the one veering off to the left, it would take us into a submaze within the grand maze. It would lead, by a twisting route with many branchings and dead ends, to the ape family, which includes gorillas and orangutans and chimpanzees.

We go to the right. That road leads to man, and it is a lonely road, because we have few fossil records to indicate the course of the earliest prehuman times. Our surveys are incomplete, our maps poor. The road takes us through uncharted and unexplored waste lands, bare of landmarks or settlements. Even with our gift of foresight, with the knowledge of all that is going to happen, we have doubts. We have gone so far and seen so little that we begin to wonder whether it is the right road after all.

It is like a trip in a remote, unfamiliar backwoods region. We move along a deserted dirt road which climbs among wild mountain places and is sometimes almost covered with grasses and shrubs. We see no farms or homes or villages. Time passes and we begin to distrust our maps and feel more and more lost. But at last, after traveling nearly two thirds of the way, we come to something alive and unusual. A hint of what lies ahead, and only a faint hint at that. We come across Oreopithecus, the "mountain ape," which turns out to be something less than an ape—and something more.

165

A stopping place on the way toward man, and a puzzle. The evidence: collections of fossils in museums, patterns in bone, parts of a larger and elusive pattern. A discovery in Tuscany, in a coal mine in the Italian village of Baccinello, not far from Pisa. At two A.M., August 2, 1958, a night-shift worker in a shaft nearly seven hundred feet below the surface was preparing for a dynamite blast. As his drill penetrated into black rock, the vibrations shook part of the roof loose. He looked up and saw something light-colored embedded in the roof, bones pressed tight between rock layers like flowers in a book.

The worker knew that the bones were important enough for him to stop work and leave them in place. Other fossils had been found in the mine. Moreover, a Swiss anthropologist was paying about forty dollars a week to encourage a continuing search for new fossils—and was staying near the village at the time to be on the spot in case of just such a discovery.

Six hours later the anthropologist himself entered the shaft, dressed in overalls and a miner's helmet. An inspection soon revealed that the fossils in the roof made up the major part of a squatting skeleton, including arm bones, ribs, backbone, pelvis and one thigh bone. The skeleton, together with the skull and missing leg bones which were found later, represented the most complete single record yet available of the structure of Oreopithecus. Soon after the preliminary inspection, the mine shaft was as crowded as a subway during rush hour.

Press photographers came and left. Reporters conducted interviews underground and, in the excitement of the moment, obtained enthusiastic stories which went somewhat beyond the facts. Headlines described "A Major Missing Link" and "A Gap in Human Evolution Filled." Artists drew pictures as he (or, rather, it) could never have been, showing nothing less than a naked white-skinned human being. To be sure, some touches were added to make things look a bit primitive. There was some hair all over the body and a low-browed forehead and a brutish face. Still, the pictures were much too flattering for a creature that existed ten to twelve million years ago.

Actually this fossil species, like many others, fits into no convenient category—and nonsense results if we stick too closely to categories in any field of science. For example, psychiatrists speak of patients suffering from schizophrenia, paranoia, or manic-depressive psychosis. But most cases are mixed and, according to one statement, "It is not a problem of what they have, but how much of each." Oreopithecus was a mixed case. It had some humanlike characteristics, such as a rounded chin and teeth that resembled human teeth in certain respects—and about an equal number of monkey characteristics.

However, it resembled an ape most of all. Anthropologists have been studying its fossil remains off and on since the late 1860's, when the first brown-stained bones and bone fragments were discovered by accident in another Tuscany coal mine. The evidence is still insufficient to settle the status of the species once and for all.

So we come across this animal during the last stages of our evolutionary journey. We have probably wandered off the main road and may soon have to retrace our steps. Now we halt near a marshy place and watch from a distance as Oreopithecus hurries by. It is moving swiftly through the tall grasses of an open area between two stretches of jungle. It is moving along mainly on all fours. Every now and then, however, it rears up on its hind legs without stopping. It looks about as it runs, because there is danger of ambush in the open and no trees are near-by for escape.

The animal turns our way for an instant. We catch a glimpse of a face and close-set eyes on the lookout. It is the face of an ape, not a man. But something about it will linger

167

in the faces of later creatures all along the line from here on. An expression just a degree too intelligent, too nearly human, to ignore for long. A wizened half-wisdom. A reminder that here is one of many creatures which did not make it, the look of a runner-up. A glimpse only. Oreopithecus reaches the jungle and disappears and we move on. The way is barren again. Only this time we do not have to travel so far to the next point of interest.

Another stopping place, another time about nine or ten million years later, another species or group of species in southern Africa. These creatures live in wide-open spaces, on great plains of coarse grasses and scarce and scattered trees. Their ancestors may have spent time swinging high among branches. If so, nature has forced them down to earth. Their forests and their jungles are thinning out. They are called Australopithecenes or "southern apes," and again the name is misleading. We have come a good deal closer to man.

These creatures include the earliest known man-apes. Full-grown adults are not impressively large, perhaps four to four and a half feet tall and weighing about eighty pounds or so. They have ape faces rather like those of chimpanzees, with flat noses, large ears, small and close-set eyes, sloping foreheads, and protruding lips and jaws which represent the last vestiges of a snout. But they hold their heads upright and not thrust forward in ape fashion. Their jaws contain teeth which are more like human than ape teeth. They have human-type feet and short stocky legs which, except for thick hair on the lower thighs and calves, appear remarkably human. Their hands have fingers too slender and fragile to walk on. They walk erect and are built to walk erect most of the time.

The man-ape may be a distinct improvement over its remote ancestors of Tuscany. But we should not overrate a creature which in certain respects has lost more than it has gained. It is an innocent abroad, a newcomer emerging into

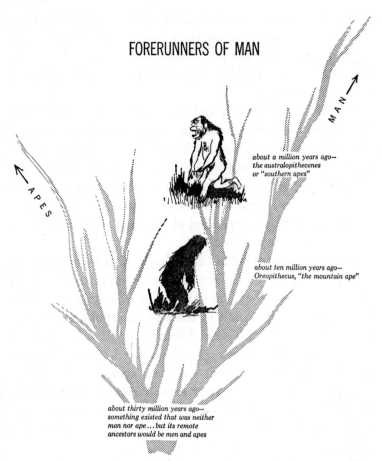

FORERUNNERS OF MAN

MAN ↗

*about a million years ago—
the australopithecenes
or "southern apes"*

*about ten million years ago—
Oreopithecus, "the mountain ape"*

APES ↖

*about thirty million years ago—
something existed that was neither
man nor ape...but its remote
ancestors would be men and apes*

an earth already inhabited by hosts of swifter and more powerful animals equipped with superior natural weapons. It is not particularly graceful or agile, and its small canine teeth are not particularly useful for fighting. The breed is born naked in a nightmare world, without dens or lairs, living out in the open.

This is an exposed breed, unsheltered among immensities. It stands upright in the flat immensity of prairies, the object of the eyes of prowlers, immersed in sounds among unseen winds and cracklings and strange cries. And another immensity sensed in a new way by a creature with a new kind of

169

brain. This breed is more aware in many ways of the open skies, clouds, the sun, moon, stars. Perhaps it feels, vague and beyond expressing, the beginnings of awe and wonder and the notion of the infinite. Man will be more articulate, but never more alone.

A world of widenesses and beasts, where the best hiding places are already occupied. There is an abundance of hiding places along the edges of plains and valleys. We move through the grasses past bare cliffs and see holes in the sides of the cliffs. And the underbrush of other cliffs conceals more holes. Caves and the mouths of caves and channels and grottoes deep inside, dissolved out of solid rock by the dripping of acid waters over the ages.

But the man-apes are not cave dwellers, at least not in the beginning. They find caves and dare to enter, for they want shelter more than they fear darkness and the unknown. Only there is blood and death in the darkness. Subhuman creatures come in and are soon driven out, and some of them never escape and are torn up and devoured. Or they live undisturbed for longer periods and learn something about living in caves, until permanent tenants return and there are more evictions and sudden deaths. Or they come in involuntarily, caught outside and dragged in dead or dying by other animals.

The caves belong to things with long teeth and claws, to killers. Man-apes are probably victims more often than victors, game to be tracked and pounced upon from the tall grasses. Going into the plains is an adventure, often perhaps an act of desperation. In search of rest and food they move mainly among third-rate territories, places difficult of access, where the killers are less likely to prowl.

For example, they move along trails winding narrowly between rocks high on the cliff edges or the slopes of bare mountains. Whenever possible they climb and run and scramble with a wall at their sides or backs, so that at least

170

one avenue of attack is eliminated. At night they huddle above plains and valleys, half-shielded under ledges and overhanging rocks. They live among other weak creatures, goats and foxes and birds and howling hyenas.

Looking at things from the negative side, we can hardly expect much of this harried, insecure breed. If we knew nothing about the dominance of change, we might envision an earth forever ruled by graceful and terrible four-footed killers. Still, there are hints of another future. The man-ape acts in a way that nothing else has acted before. Its hands are freed and capable of intricate manipulations. Its brain is small compared to what will come, not much larger than the brain of a newborn human infant, but rather advanced for the times. This is a new brain, and it will develop and play an outstanding part in the future. It will make possible an entirely new trend in evolution. In fact, it will change—and change radically—the very nature of evolution.

The gray matter of the cortex has developed into a network of several billion nerve cells, a superstructure with new possibilities. The cortex is a system of patterns, electrical circuits or pathways for the flow of signals. The patterns are not rigid. They can be altered by the impact of the outside world. Sensations, signals from the outside world, stream into the nervous system and produce changes among its cells and fibers. The changes are new circuits or patterns shaped inside the skull. Because of them the cortex sends new combinations of signals to the muscles—and the messages give rise to new patterns, action patterns or patterns of behavior. To put it another way, altered behavior in the outside world is an expression of altered circuits in the brain.

Imagine a robot, a simple electronic Frankenstein monster, which walks in straight lines only. By tinkering with its circuitry, altering its built-in wiring system, engineers change its behavior so that now it makes detours and avoids obstacles. Nature's way is more subtle. There is no need for tinkering. The brain changes itself automatically on the basis of experience, the analyzed past. In other words, animals learn and remember, and man-apes have the capacity to learn and remember better than any of their fellow species.

Man-apes go about in packs or groups. Weak and frightened as individuals, they find a feeling of strength and a measure of security in the mass. From their places on cliffs and mountainsides, from their high seats on balconies of rock, they watch and see many things. Spectators. Spectators on the verge of participating more violently and more fully than any species has ever participated before. Down below along river banks are fine hunting grounds. Killers crouch and wait here, where their prey must come to them. Herds of animals come to drink, and some die while their heads are lowered. After the killers have eaten their fill and gone, the scavengers move in. Vultures come down and tear at what remains and stay clear of the hyenas.

Man-apes observe. They are by nature vegetarian, a quality they share with every ape, and meat is distasteful. But they go hungry too often. Their food situation is precarious. These are not the most abundant of times, and fruits and juicy leaves and shoots are more and more scarce. Driven by hunger the ape-men come down from the rocks, drive off the hyenas and vultures, and consume the remains of dead animals and drink or suck the blood. They adapt. They are vegetarians in the first stages of corruption. They become scavengers, too.

This is a plausible line of development. It is a reconstruction of the past, like the body of a primeval creature deduced from pieces of a skeleton. Another piecing together of evidence into a pattern, like the task of building a double-helix model of the genetic substance DNA. Our theories are based on masses of excavated records. Detailed studies of the cusps and grinding surfaces and grooves in teeth, the shapes and structures of bones found among rocks of different geological

172

ages, the habits and customs of monkeys and apes and primitive peoples alive today. Measurement, observation, tentative inference to fill in the gaps—and discoveries one after the other.

Workers exploded dynamite in a quarry near the village of Taungs, South Africa. Solid rock was shattered into fragments, and one of the fragments contained a small skull. The skull of a chimpanzee, gorilla cub, or subhuman child? The experts disagreed. That was in 1924. A dozen years later, a shift of scene to the Sterkfontein Valley and neighboring valleys in the Transvaal. This is a region of cliffs, and of caves which twist through the cliffs like the passageways of burrowing things.

There were places in the caves where you could stand up, and places you had to crawl or sidle or squeeze through. Grottoes and chambers and low narrow tunnels like ratholes, all wet and slippery. Caves and tourists, a minor industry to supplement quarrying. Guides with flashlights kept you moving and talked incessantly, providing half-information and damp jokes. They led the way along safe routes, and past pitch-dark crevices which went on and on into the depths and were closed to the public. Souvenirs were sold to the tourists on the way out, mostly old bones and teeth and perhaps a whole jaw or skull if the price was right.

Small businessmen and tourists came first. Anthropologists came later and found many fossils in the forbidden, blocked-off passageways. Some of the fossils had been washed into crevices and grottoes from other places. Others spilled in during ancient cave-ins; still others were the remains of cave-dwelling animals and their victims. More findings. Fossils from more than a hundred individual man-apes living in different times and under different conditions. And among the fossils were signs of something new.

In one cave, for example, searchers found an unexpected combination of fossils involving three different creatures.

173

Two of the creatures were represented by the most solid evidence of all, enduring bone. A baboon's skull and the thighbone of an antelope. There were no bones representing the third creature, no objects, no tangible remains. Only insubstantial inference, indirect evidence as meaningful as bone. The third creature was absent but accounted for. The baboon skull had two broken places in it, two jagged holes. The thighbone of the antelope had two joints at the end, two "bumps," which fitted neatly into the holes. Apparently a third party, a man-ape, had wielded the long bone and cracked the skull open to get at the brains inside.

One clue among others, suggesting that certain subhuman African breeds used tools. In the beginning they probably took things as they found them, ready-made and close at hand and on the spur of the moment. Not only bones but branches to serve as clubs and perhaps branches with thorns to ward off scavengers, and stones. Stones to bash and scrape with, or to hurl in rage and terror. Natural implements located conveniently close in times of need and emergency.

We move on beyond the scavengers and tool users. We move toward man among mists and see things now and then only when the mists clear, for there are still many gaps in the record. Time passes, a brief interval in the evolution of matter, a period ten or more times longer than that from the pyramids to the United Nations building. During this period the balance of power is shifting. Other varieties of man-apes, and the descendants of the "southern apes" and more manlike species, become more restless and more dangerous.

It is partly a matter of taste. They begin to acquire a taste for flesh, a growing desire and a growing lust. They want the food of the killers, and not just the leavings. They want and dare and learn. Over the centuries and millennia they change from scavengers to killers, and suffer and die and triumph in new ways. The hunt for meat on the hoof is a battle to the death, a contest of brains and instincts so demanding that it will take men to win it once and for all.

174

The prey includes animals such as deer and antelopes and wild horses. They are already highly developed, always on the alert, always ready for trouble. The crackling of a twig or a sudden movement a hundred yards away or a warning odor in the wind is enough to put them to flight. Millions of years ago their ancestors were less alert and less fleet of foot. They tried many futile ways of escaping, many dodges that did not fool their enemies. It took millions and millions of deaths to evolve creatures with sharp senses and fast reflexes. What remains and flourishes is the cream of the crop, the products of a weeding-out process.

The hunters are also products of weeding out. But they contain the seed of a different kind of change, an evolution which has yet to come into its own, an evolution by learning. The challenge of the chase—the very fleetness and resourcefulness of the prey—acts as a goad to further and faster learning. The hunt becomes an organic force which pushes the horizon further and further out. The hunters wander more widely about the world—a habit which we, their descendants, have never lost even though we no longer go on the prowl in quite the same way.

Apes and monkeys are essentially stay-at-homes, for all their chattering and restlessness. They are curious about things, but not in a roving way. They generally remain in relatively small territories, and their horizons and possibilities are limited. Baboons rarely travel more than a few miles from the places where they sleep at night. Other monkeys, and gibbons, tend to move within restricted parts of the forest, and colonies often live among the familiar leaves and branches of a single tree. The creatures that are becoming men roam far and wide. They must if they are to satisfy their persisting and growing needs. They are driven largely by their desire for red, raw meat.

Adventurers and explorers, they travel to new places for food. They do more hiding and watching, at the edges of forests or from strange hills and cliffs. They learn more and

175

more about the habits of other killers. They watch death coming inch by inch in the form of things crawling closer on their bellies. They watch death waiting before the leap and staying on the right side of the wind. They imitate the experts and develop new varieties of stealth.

Generations and generations of hunters, former underdogs on the make, driven by a desire that knowledge never slakes completely. Failures and successes. Good luck and bad, but usually remembered luck, luck puzzled over and stored for future reference. Knowledge accumulating, spiraling in the familiar way that marks us still, bringing new satisfactions and new desires and new frustrations and the sad and glorious need for new knowledge. The brain with its newly conceived ideas—a growing seed, a spur sharper than thorn, the restlessness of an unborn child kicking in the womb.

The future becomes longer and more meaningful. Hunters observe cycles that are not their cycles, and enter the cycles and learn to move with them. Seasons and the mass migrations of herds. Animals moving with the weather and with the rising and setting of the sun. Long rhythms and short rhythms which move groups of hunters and hunted together the way tides in the sea move drifting stuff on the surface. Species and complexes of species on the go together.

The hunters are subtly more aware of all this and look increasingly into the future. They learn new ways of going, not to places where the herds are, but to silent and empty places where the herds will be in a few hours or a few days. They wait for longer and longer periods and the waiting brings results. Successful foresight is the science or the magic of these times, depending upon whether the prophets share or withhold the reasons for their prophecies.

The one and the many, the individual and the group. Hunting alone, the solo flight into the wilderness, is often successful. But even the best hunter needs the group. He can go out on his own, follow trails and stalk his prey, and obtain enough food to fill his stomach. When he returns, however, less skilled hunters may grumble and plot; there may be killing within the colony. Furthermore, hunting together is even more successful than hunting alone. Generally speaking, ten hunters with a group plan can do a good deal more killing per capita than ten solo hunters. The dream of self-sufficiency, the cosy Robinson Crusoe dream, dies hard. Or, rather, it is being modified, for it has never died. In any case, the other dream, the group dream, is shaping itself more clearly.

The climax of watching and predicting and joining arrives when the hunters come within striking distance of their prey. This is the pay-off, the moment of culmination. The waiting is over and killing must be done. Everything available is used for weapons, bare hands and stones and heavy branches and bones. All ready-made stuff at first, a selection of sharper and sharper objects. There is an increasing need for things that do more than stun, that draw blood like horns and hooves.

Then, as the hunt evolves, over the ages and slowly and imperceptibly as usual, the most significant change of all. The brain is at work. Barrages of sensation keep streaming into the cortex, buzzing signals, incessant goading and the flowering of a peculiar sort of restless dissatisfaction. The hunters cannot stand pat or live with things as they are. They are already too deeply committed. Their ancestors were not content with leftover flesh, and they are not content with natural objects lying on the ground. They think and begin shaping matter to suit their ends. Bit by bit they change from simple tool users, creatures which depend on ready-made implements, to tool-makers.

As far as obtaining evidence is concerned, the transition may be extremely difficult to detect. Investigators have examined large quantities of stones found at ancient sites and have not always been able to tell which are which, which are natural or begotten objects and which are made by hands. Imagine looking through a pile of newly collected stones, a rubble heap of flints and pebbles and rocky chunks. The odds are that the great majority of them are the work of nature.

They have been shaped blindly and accidentally by inanimate forces. Swirled and broken in whirlpools, rolled smooth by waves of oceans long since receded, ground together in creeping soils and beneath glaciers, fractured and chipped by ice masses floating in shallow seas. Among all the shapes some inevitably look like cutting edges and the heads of axes and hammers. Coincidences, false clues, chance shapes which have always been formed and will always be formed as long as waters move and the earth heaves. Fragments which represent neither beginnings nor endings. They simply exist as they have always existed.

But somewhere in the pile, mixed among all the debris, are a few objects of a very different sort. They are true beginnings, things with a future, first things which will lead to more delicate and more complicated instruments. They are made by hands. They will evolve as the brains that move the hands evolve. They will evolve with the evolution of ideas. Indeed, they are ideas, or, more concretely, examples of the only kind of ideas that we can trace for certain in remote times—ideas embodied in works, in specific objects shaped for reasons. They are ideas and strivings and hopes expressed in rock, like epitaphs on tombstones.

Somewhere in the pile are things with purposes, "eoliths," the earliest made implements of a new kind of animal. We cannot always identify them. Sometimes they merge indistinguishably with unevolving, accidentally formed fragments. We are in another borderline zone, and the evidence is often obscure. One prehistorian summarizes the problem as follows: "Man made one, God made ten thousand—God help the man who tries to see the one in the ten thousand."

178

A RECENT FOSSIL DISCOVERY

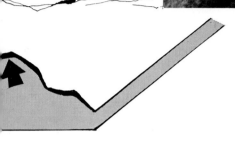

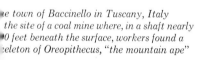

...e town of Baccinello in Tuscany, Italy
...the site of a coal mine where, in a shaft nearly
...0 feet beneath the surface, workers found a
...celeton of Oreopithecus, "the mountain ape"

CAVES

Transitions are never easy to work out. But we see the broad differences before and after. Looking back, we see some of the forces that shaped our ancestors. Walking erect and the freeing of the hands, the increasing need for meat and then the desire for meat, the rise of hunting and the whole complex of activities that went with it. Hunting provided the last big "push" which accelerated the coming of man. Our remote ancestors had good brains, but not the sort of brains we know. The great expansion of the brain, the swelling of the cerebral hemispheres and the spread of the cortex over the surfaces, came with the development of hunting.

Every activity associated with the chase, from the plans that preceded trips into the wilderness to the final kill, favored the most intelligent as well as the strongest and swiftest hunters. Creatures with bigger and better brains, the bearers of favorable genes, outlived and outbred their contemporaries. Larger brains required a longer time to develop, so infants were helpless longer after birth. The period of helplessness increased from about two years for apes toward the six to eight years for man. Extended maternal care, the extra importance of the male as protector and provider, and new patterns of shelter and family living were indirect results of the acquired taste for raw meat, one of our numerous original sins.

Nearly human creatures, submen, learned slowly by present-day standards. The early evolution of the chase took some 300,000 years, and this is a conservative estimate. It could have taken twice as long. In any case, the basic techniques and attitudes of hunting, the basic "carnivore psychology," were fully established at least half a million years ago. That brings us to another landmark, very close to home. On our reduced time scale for cosmic history it is now about four seconds before midnight. The first men are about to appear on earth.

179

Human Beings
of Prehistory
11

WE are coming out of the borderline zone between man-ape and man, a misty transition period of prehistory. For a long time, long before the coming of man, a new kind of evolution has been emerging from and along with the old. The old evolution is by no means unimportant or obsolete. Indeed, it is operating in full swing. It is operating on small groups which belong to species occupying large territories, live relatively isolated from one another, and may from time to time meet and interbreed.

Each group is a natural experiment. Hunters go about in troops of perhaps 75 to 150 individuals and breed closely among themselves. The times are ripe for rapid weeding out. Mutations tend to show up quickly and obviously, within a few generations. Unfavorable mutations are eliminated, as many hunters are killed by animals that fight back. Death rates are high and so is the premium on rare favorable mutations. Similar conditions may have prevailed long ago when fish began crawling on land, or when birds and mammals evolved from reptiles.

But now there is also another evolution which depends less completely on genes and mutants and natural selection. The beginnings of advanced culture, represented by tool-making. A ready-made tool is a kind of accessory limb or organ which genes have not shaped. Creatures have used this sort of implement before. The Galápagos "woodpecker" finch modifies its beak by gripping a thorn and prying insects out of the bark of trees, and monkeys may use rocks to crack nuts open. A tool shaped deliberately to a design, however crude, is an accessory that may evolve without the benefit of new, favorable mutants.

Such developments come very slowly at first. Among the earliest handmade tools that can be identified positively are pebbles split to obtain a cutting or scraping edge. If you happened to notice one of these objects lying among other broken rocks on the floor of a cave, you might or might not bother to pick it up. Only an expert would recognize it on sight for what it is. But you would certainly pick up a more refined tool, say, a flint with a sharp point and a clean, sharp cutting edge. To go from the pebble to the flint tool requires the gradually accumulating experience of several hundred thousands of years. These tools are the works of men.

New power comes with tools and weapons, deliberately made and improved. Hunters can enter caves more often now and stay longer. But they must fight bitterly and continually to hold the caves, even temporarily. Bears and tigers and other killers have to be driven out and kept out. A cave is no place to be cornered in when beasts try to re-enter. The danger is particularly great at night, in the shadows and the darkness, despite the vigilance of sentinels. Death often comes suddenly at night—that is, until fires burn on the first hearths and the darkness is shattered as it was with the shining of the first stars.

First experiences of fire. Early man knows fire before he uses it. He sees it from a ledge at a distance. A storm forms on the horizon, where grasses merge with sky, at the other side of a prairie. He watches. Smoke bursts like thunderclouds out of a mountaintop, and makes sounds like thunder rumblings or the roars of wild animals. The skies above the mountain are thick with smoke clouds. A glow comes from the crater, as if a sun or a moon were caught in the mountain and trying to rise. Then something red wells up at the crater lip and spills over the edge like many streams after heavy rains. The streams move down in slow-motion cascades, crushing and consuming forests in front of them and in a wide swath on either side.

Or the storm breaks much closer. The mountain where men seek shelter rumbles and shakes underground and rocks collapse, and there are flights and some of the people are trapped and consumed in red streams along with the forest. Or bolts of lightning, cracks in a splitting storm-sky, strike the ground in a crackling electrical hiss and the ground goes wild with light. The light dances and travels among bushes and trees, or in strange-smelling places where oil oozes at the surface. Animals rush away from the spreading light, and the people rush away.

But before the light dies some of the people return. They may be merely curious, or perhaps they have observed something. Perhaps they remember the panic of their enemies as well as their own panic. Perhaps they remember animals running away—and among them the killers that make the caves dangerous. Out of the confusion and the chaos and blind terror of the unknown, an observation stands out sharp, like a knife hurled and stuck and still vibrating in the trunk of a tree. Out of the terror an idea condenses. A thing of the mind takes shape like a star or a planet condensing in a nebula or a crystal in cooling lava.

Some of the people return and dare to come close and

touch embers or feel flame on their skins. They are burned and hurt and run away and listen to the I-told-you-so's of the others. They return, run away again and again, and learn. At last, at the ends of dry branches or on flattened lumps of clay, they bring fire back with them. Now for the first time man begins to move into the caves and stays there. Fire is a new weapon that bites deeper than the edges of split stone. Fire is a devil turned god which the killers fear. The killers retreat and are routed and man becomes a cave dweller in the full sense.

Fire is a new light in the wilderness. At night, from a distance, animals moving among trees see lights at the mouths of many caves. Not lights spreading wild, out of control. But spots of light that stay put, concentrated spots with a purpose. Fire is a new wall. Behind the wall men find new security, new patterns of being together in the night, huddlings around a center, family circles or the beginnings of family circles. There is more time to play and work and plan and share ideas, less sleep, perhaps. The days are made longer behind the new walls.

Fire is a thing to be fed, a new mouth. It must be replenished continually, so reserves of branches and twigs and broken logs are piled in corners and dead-end passages of caves. It is like a lighthouse beacon over dangerous waters, or an Olympic torch signifying victory. It must not be allowed to die out. When fires fall too low or stop burning, the jungle starts prowling and growling back toward the caves. Fire hunters go out to seek more fuel or fresh flames. Fire is a new freedom, an unleashing. Without heat of his own, man flourished best in Africas. Now he can take a climate with him and explore more widely and migrate out of the tropics.

These are some of the trends and events our findings suggest. Evolving patterns of behavior are another phase of the search for records of prehistory. The trail leads northward to a cave on Dragon's Mountain in China, about thirty miles from Peking. The first skull of an early representative of the genus Homo was found in the cave more than thirty years ago, and investigators unearthed many more fossil remains after that. Peking man had an appreciably larger and more human-looking head than the man-apes, and a forehead that sloped less. His brain was about twice as large as theirs and, on the size scale, occupies a position roughly halfway between the brains of apes and of men alive today.

The first known hearths blazed on the floors of his caves. Red-yellow clays, baked solid as brick, and charred seeds and bones and antlers indicate where his fires burned. Although we know little about his dietary habits, he was probably no cook and ate his meat raw. He cracked bones and skulls for the nourishment inside, and, judging by fossilized scraps found at his dining sites, some of those bones and skulls belonged to his own kind. He was a cannibal upon occasion, a practice which may not have been uncommon among early hunters and cave dwellers.

Peking man was making workmanlike tools at least half a million years ago. His tool kit included heavy scrapers or cleavers, choppers resembling hand axes, pointed implements for prying and picking, and flake tools which had sharp cutting edges and were carefully chipped off larger blocks of stone. Some anthropologists have learned to duplicate such work. In the process of shaping stubborn pieces of volcanic rock and quartz, they have mashed and cut their fingers more than once. They vouch for the fact that making stone tools required considerable skill, and speak with respect of the traditions of "flake-and-chopper-tool industries."

These traditions, more strongly than any other evidence, imply that Peking man talked. The size of his brain also suggests a capacity for speech. But even without that hint it would be difficult to conceive of tool-making techniques being conveyed by grunts, cries, gestures or anything short of language. According to some estimates, tool-making and all

184

that went with it called for a vocabulary of at least several hundred words. New methods and new tools called for new words.

Experience accumulated so that it took longer and longer to learn what there was to know, and, perhaps for the first time, people too old to do active work became useful members of the group. One scientist speculates that "probably no man ever reached the age of sixty until language attained such importance in the equipment of the species that long experience became valuable in a man who could neither fight nor hunt." The rise of language helped foster the rise of patriarchs, sages and elder statesmen.

Other breeds of men lived half a million or more years ago. They did not differ markedly from Peking man, and most of them were members of the same widespread species. They hunted in Java, Germany, Africa and probably elsewhere. As in the more remote past, evolution was not a matter of one species giving rise to another in a neat sequence. Species overlapped one another and mixed and produced many varieties that did not survive. Peking man and other early breeds probably coexisted with man-apes for thousands of generations before the man-apes vanished.

The first true representatives of Homo sapiens may have appeared as much as 300,000 years ago, or some fifteen hundred centuries before Neanderthal man. We do not know why they failed to dominate the earth sooner, except that dominating has always taken time. Mammals required millions of years to spread widely after evolving from reptiles, and on such a time scale a few hundred thousand years is a mere handful of yesterdays.

Before our kind established themselves they shared the earth with others, including Neanderthal man. During the summer of 1856 a skeleton was found in the Neanderthal Valley near Düsseldorf, Germany. This discovery, which came three years before the publication of *On the Origin of*

Species, marked the start of scientific studies of human evolution. It was to become a familiar story: quarrying in a limestone cave high on a cliffside, dynamite blasts, and workers noticing old bones among the rubble. Since then the remains of similar men have been found in other countries.

As "Darwin's first witness for human evolution," Neanderthal man has become famous. He has also been maligned not only in popular accounts of anthropology but in practically all textbooks, including the latest editions. The very word "Neanderthal" suggests a brutal half-gorilla, a smaller version of King Kong. The textbooks describe him as "uncouth and repellent," "ungraceful in form," "coarsely built." They harp particularly on his supposed inability to walk erect, and claim that he shuffled along with knees bent and an awkward, uncertain gait. These accounts are based largely on a study of a skeleton found in France half a century ago—and the skeleton turns out to have been that of an old man with a severe case of arthritis.

Neanderthal man was not outstandingly lovely to look at, but he was in no sense subhuman. His brain was probably larger than ours, although brain size is not the only criterion of intelligence, and certain higher nerve centers may not yet have evolved fully in him. Furthermore, he walked erect. In fact, a recent report indicates that his appearance was not unduly shocking: "If he could be reincarnated and placed in a New York subway—providing that he were bathed, shaved and dressed in modern clothing—it is doubtful whether he would attract any more attention than some of its other denizens."

Neanderthal stopped at nothing in his drive for meat, going after the toughest animals alive—mammoths, woolly rhinoceroses and other big game. He developed new patterns of weapons and strategies. His designs and needs became more and more complex. He threw spears with stone tips at running targets, and made large, sharp flake implements by a special technique which involved marking out the desired forms beforehand on stone cores shaped like turtles' shells.

One of his most ingenious weapons was the bola, a set of three rounded stones attached by thongs and still used in Argentina today. You hold one stone in your hand, whirl the other two stones faster and faster, and then let go, aiming at the legs of an escaping animal. If your aim is good, the thongs wind around the animal's legs and tie them up so that you can close in for the kill. The hunted were more powerful and faster than the hunters, but that was not enough to save them.

These people were upsetting the "natural" order of things, changing the world to suit themselves. A growing independence, a species relying somewhat less on randomness and what the elements happened to bring. Peking man had taken fire as he found it, ready-made fires set by lava or lightning. Neanderthal man conquered fire in a new and more complete sense. He learned to produce his heat and light artificially. To ignite kindling material he probably struck two stones together, a trick he may have discovered while making tools.

Patterns, but not patterns like galactic spirals or the facets of crystals or the limbs and bodies of more ancient species. Shaped objects are artificial patterns which tell us something about what Neanderthal man did. There are also artificial patterns, codes or messages of a kind, which tell us something about what he believed. Such patterns, perhaps the most impressive of all, indicate that he made sacrifices and buried at least some of his dead and perhaps worshiped. The beginnings of religion may be traced to records found in the caves of the big-game hunters.

The evolution of ideas about death. At one time in prehistory the causes of most deaths must have been violent and obvious—natural, "ready-made" catastrophes. Floods and

187

eruptions, a fall on a slippery trail and the drop over the cliff edge, the attack of a bear or tiger on the hunt. Or primeval versions of more complex violence to come, the precursors of war, fights among man-ape scavengers that had not learned to share. At one time, endings with less obvious causes, deaths from disease and aging, may have been regarded as malicious acts or punishments, the doings of evil or good spirits.

Ages must have passed before some individuals began to understand the rules of the game. They began to realize that no matter how they lived, no matter what taboos they observed or how successfully they avoided ill luck and injury, they would die. We can only speculate on how man evolved interpretations of what happens after he ceases to move and breathe. But he has left clues in the caves, in the dark. He has left messages among tapering columns and rippled curtains of rock, among fantastic crystal formations.

A cave at the edge of the Mediterranean, at the foot of a mountain between Naples and Rome. You clamber down a steep footpath and come to the cave near the surf. The mouth is high and wide-open and arched, and you can see deep inside. You enter a chamber as large as an auditorium, and hear the surf behind as you walk in. Inside, where it is darker, there are three holes leading deeper into the base of the mountain. Most tourists stop here, because they would get their clothes dirty if they went further.

One of the holes is so small that you have to crawl through it on your stomach, and keep crawling for about twenty or thirty feet. Then you are in a grotto. People have been here: a few tourists, scientists, and boys, who are the most active explorers of all. People were here at least 60,000 years before the birth of Christ. This is a burial site, the site of one important finding. A Neanderthal skeleton laid inside a circle of stones, a magic ring, a pattern as startling as a shout in a church, among the natural crystal patterns of the grotto. Another tomb, another epitaph. It is like hearing a strange language and trying to deduce what you can from the gestures, a pantomime or a charade in stone. And near-by, crude stone vessels filled with the bones of animals.

Similar graves and vessels in other caves all hint at the same theme, the idea behind the patterns. When the vessels were originally laid in place, the bones had flesh on them. Joints and cuts of meat for the nourishment of the dead in the after life. Warmth and light for the dead; hearths found near some of the graves. Also near-by, tools and weapons for the dead. And more than that, mystery patterns.

Stone boxes, prehistoric treasure chests, with the skulls of cave bears in them and bones stuck into the eye sockets and jaws of the skulls. Alcoves and recesses in the walls containing cave-bear skulls in neat rows and piles. Things put in places with a design, an intent. Intimations of cave-bear cults and rites and dances around skulls set on poles. Ceremonies for spirits of the dead and for other spirits—spirits which would evolve, with time and the evolution of the brain, into gods and God.

The Neanderthalers and their rituals disappeared about fifty to seventy-five thousand years ago. But before that people like ourselves were already increasing their numbers and taking over the main line of human evolution. They differed from us only in minor ways. Their brains were practically the same as ours, and given an equivalent education, they could have designed machines and performed experiments as sophisticated as ours. They had fishhooks and harpoons and the bow and arrow, a machine that may have helped speed the extinction of Neanderthal man. They sprinkled their dead with red powder, perhaps to restore a semblance of the flush of life, and their religious ceremonies were generally more elaborate than those of preceding species.

But if we had nothing else from them, their works of art would be more than enough. Neanderthal man probably developed his own artistic traditions, although no traces have been found. The cave artists did something as magnificent and daring as anything that has happened since. Modern explorers go into caves with full regalia and equipment, crash helmets and warm clothing and fluorescent nylon ropes and floodlights and winches to lower them into the deepest crevices. They have relatively few illusions and do not regard caves as haunts for ghosts and demons. Yet it requires considerable nerve to climb and crawl and swim and dive in underground places. Even the experts have felt flashes of panic, and have died in their panic.

The explorers of yesterday walked in a haunted night. They were trespassing into regions where beasts and the spirits of beasts existed. They must have seen and heard many things on the long way in, and their imagination did the rest, feeding on superstition and the darkness and shadows that moved as the lights passed. Some of them lost their way and never returned. If it takes courage for us, it must have taken a great deal more for them. But they were driven by forces strong enough to justify the risks and the terrors— by curiosity and, above all, by a belief in the power of ritual.

They performed their ceremonies in secret places. They went down and down through mazes of limestone formations, far from cave entrances, for long journeys as much as two miles beneath the surface of the earth. We have followed them and found some of the places where they stopped and worked by the light of torches and lamps with moss or fiber wicks sputtering in animal fat. Figures painted and engraved on the walls of grottoes and passageways. A five-year-old girl found the first prehistoric painting about eighty years ago during an exploring trip with her father in a cave near a castle in Altamira, Spain. She wandered into a small chamber which her father had missed and called out to him and pointed. It was a dying bison, painted beautifully in red.

Hundreds of paintings have been discovered since then,

often in the least accessible places. In one cave, near the village of Trois Frères in southern France, you have to crawl for more than an hour in damp muddy passages with low, jagged rocks to bump your head against. Then you come to a whole picture gallery of animals and, still further on, to a "self-portrait" of the artist, whom you cannot see because he wears a reindeer mask and a bear's paws and the tail of a horse.

Much of what we are today can be traced back to the caves and the people who lived there. The buried past. Churches and temples, art galleries and cemeteries evolved in places underground—many of which have not been discovered and will never be discovered. Fireplaces and furnaces are the open hearths of early man brought up to date. Our living rooms are their grottoes transformed, modern versions of the chambers in which they came together around fires at night. Our closets and attics have come from the dark corners and alcoves where they put skins and food and fuel for the fires and rock-and-bone symbols of their beliefs.

Most of our genes are their genes, the genes of the cave painters. And our gene pools may also include exact duplicates of some of the reproducing molecules passed along through thousands of generations of men who had not evolved as far as the cave painters. In Israel, about fifteen miles from Haifa on the shore road to Tel-Aviv, you drive past ploughed fields and groves of olive trees and limestone cliffs dry yellow-brown in the blazing sun. You see the dark entrances of caves in the cliffs.

This is the region of Mount Carmel, where Elijah slew the prophets of Baal, and where a mixed population of human beings lived around 75,000 B.C. Fossil bones indicate that some of them looked like Neanderthalers. Others represent a stage in between Neanderthalers and people like ourselves; still others were much closer to us in appearance and brain capacity. It seems that Mount Carmel was a meeting place,

191

a melting pot where Neanderthal men and modern-type men from Africa came together and interbred. We have been hybrids, mongrels, for a long time.

Burial rites and art represent high points of the first and by far the longest stage in human history. Our records speak mainly of life in caves, an existence which lasted at least half a million years and perhaps closer to a million years. The first stage occupies more than ninety-nine percent of the total time from the earliest men to ourselves.

During this stage there have been two parallel evolutions: the old-time, natural-selection evolution which is as ancient as life itself, the evolution of the organism, man, which we know by his fossil remains, his stained and broken bones; and the evolution of the works and ideas of man, known by handmade things often found among the fossils. Two parallel evolutions. The past is like a panoramic photograph, fuzzy in the background and clearer as you come up forward.

Looking back, we see through the haze of the far distance the vague forms, the half-shadows, of men with crude faces like chimpanzees—and in the foreground, clear and in fine focus, the human face. In the far distance, vague and crudely worked stones some of which are difficult to identify as tools or weapons—and in the foreground, unmistakable patterns, blades and barbs and axes and arrowheads.

The second stage began only about ten thousand years ago. On our twenty-four-hour time scale for the shaping of matter, that represents one tenth of a second before midnight, midnight being the present. In man and through man the shaping of matter picks up tremendous speed. The process is still smooth and continuous, step by step. Developments do not spring into being suddenly. They grow and emerge out of simpler beginnings. Trial and error take place everywhere —indeed, more than ever before. There are still branchings and discarded experiments and false starts. But the entire pace of things is stepped up.

From here on the new evolution flourishes or, rather, the most recent kind of evolution—evolution by culture. The most important factor during the earliest times of man, and at least two billion years before that during the earliest times of life, has been changes in genes. Changes in the structure of crystal-like DNA helixes passed on like family jewels from generation to generation. These are invisible events which we do not control, and in many ways we are what they make us. But during the past hundred centuries or so, the really big changes have taken place outside ourselves and our inherited molecules.

We see the earliest signs of evolution by culture far down among the hierarchies of living things. Animals learn and their young imitate, and some information is passed along and preserved. But now the pace is quickening. We thumb through snapshots, through sample sites and excavations in the album of the very recent past. Every snapshot shows new beginnings and new transitions.

A cave, again on the slopes of Mount Carmel. Tools include a sickle of stone, probably to reap grain growing wild. After fighting to get into caves, after half a million years of cave dwelling, people are just beginning to venture a little way out of the entrance. It is like a turtle peeping out from under its shell, or a primeval fish crawling and gulping a few feet from the water's edge. There is a terrace in front of the cave, and stones arranged in curving rows and perhaps some stone benches. And here, right out in the open and surrounded by a ring of stones, is a hearth. The fireside has migrated from the cave, but not the makers of fire—not yet.

A camp site in the Kurdish hills of Iraq, a few thousand years later. These people have moved out of the caves and live in the open. And another new development. The meat men ate had always come from wild animals. Now the hunt becomes less vital, the supply of meat more reliable. The campers have domesticated animals, or at least live among

193

animals that can be domesticated, such as sheep and goats and pigs. But as recent refugees from caves, they have not yet learned to stay put. They are wanderers, prehistoric gypsies. Their stopping place is not a village and not a farm, although it includes some traces of both. It will soon be deserted.

Near the abandoned camp, also in the Kurdish hills, but later, about 6500 B.C., the earliest known village, Jarmo. The site of a revolution long in the making, the most significant step since the shaping of tools. But it comes so quickly, compared with the old pace of things, that it is upon us and beyond us, almost before we know what is happening. Like a jet plane streaking by, and we hardly have time to applaud. The people of Jarmo have taken root. They are growing their own food in their own back yard. Plants and animals tamed and bred and cultivated; barley, wheat, peas, sheep, oxen, pigs, goats. Food collectors have become food producers.

Taking root gives evolution another push. Now a series of snapshots in the Tigris-Euphrates Valley of southern Mesopotamia. Tepe Gawra—a town with a temple and a market place, metal axes and sickles, painted pottery, irrigated fields and an expanding foreign trade. All significant developments, all coming within a span of a thousand years or so after Jarmo. Warka—site of the White Temple, which took at least five years to design and build, a great pattern. And pictograph patterns on clay tablets which represent a step before the first writing. The valley of the Nile—the rise of Egypt and dynasties and empires and armies.

Civilization is an abused term, and some of the historians who talk about it most tend to abuse it most. But the oldest political complexes of efficient agriculture and cities and monumental art arose from foundations laid in the Near East by people identified as "basic Mediterranean types with minor Negroid characteristics." The oldest civilizations we know appeared in the Near East around 3500 B.C. and perhaps in India at almost the same time, in China about 1500 B.C., and in Central America and the Andes regions of the Mayas about 500 B.C. They mark the end of prehistory. For more recent times we have increasingly complete records.

The third stage of human evolution started an instant ago, an instant consisting of three or four centuries. It includes the rise of a new profession, science, and the Industrial Revolution, which is just gathering momentum. It has brought a clearer and clearer picture of ourselves and our past, and it has been a battle every inch of the way. Sometimes learning comes so hard that we begin to wonder whether that is actually what we were made for.

As late as the eighteenth century some scientists still doubted the existence of fossils. The bones were not really bones but the results of a natural shaping force, a "seminal gust" which turned rocks and soil into things which looked like bones. Wiser investigators who felt this theory was nonsense often misinterpreted what they found. One of them claimed that eight black bones imbedded in a stone on Gallows Hill in Altdorf, Germany, were the remains of a human sinner drowned in the Flood. Many years passed before the bones were identified as the vertebrae of a "giant salamander."

The discovery of Neanderthal man was greeted with a chorus of learned disbelief. Most scientists found themselves in agreement on one point only: he was certainly not one of our prehistoric ancestors. Beyond that they were undecided. A German professor suggested that he was a Cossack killed during a Russian invasion of 1814. Others called him "an old Dutchman" and "a member of the Celtic race." A leading authority consulted medical men and announced that Neanderthal man was a recent specimen stricken by bone-deforming diseases.

Not long after that, it was the turn of the cave-paintings in Altamira. This is one of the most flagrant cases of disbe-

195

lief in the history of science. The paintings were denounced as bogus. According to general opinion, a contemporary artist had visited the cave and done the work on the sly. In collusion with the owner of the cave, he was perpetrating a colossal fraud on mankind. The experts, like some of the astronomers invited to look through Galileo's telescopes, would not even come to see for themselves.

We note and italicize our old prejudices. Moving swiftly in the stream of evolving stuff, we wonder what prejudices hold us back today and we learn because we must. New evidence pours in as we learn. The milk teeth of a child who lived in Tanganyika, Africa, some five hundred thousand years ago. A storm causes a small landslide in an excavation in southern France, and a student notices a dislodged stone with the figure of a woman engraved on it. A bas-relief of a "fertility goddess" fashioned about 20,000 B.C.

A system of several hundred caves, among the largest in the world, explored in Borneo near oil fields on the coast of the South China Sea. In one of the caves, just above a dark tunnel where an underground river plunges down into the heart of the limestone, an exciting find. A fleet of eighteen wooden "death ships" with tiger-dragons carved on the prows. Funeral vessels placed near the river for the last journeys of the dead. A death-ship ritual four to five thousand years old.

These are a few sample discoveries, all reported recently during a single month. We go after our past, and meet it everywhere and more and more often as the search accelerates. The search, the incessant gathering of knowledge in all fields, is the unique mark of our species—the most spectacular feature of the new beginning which is the third stage in the story of man.

Evolution in

Our Times

12

THE story of the past as we conceive it today. Ten billion years lie behind us, a wake of yesterdays trailing off into time. Ten billion years of the shaping of substance. Inanimate shapings first, from a cloud of disorganized stuff to stars, galaxies, planets, moons, crystals. Then cloud stuff evolved into increasingly subtle patterns, from inanimate to animate—reproducing molecules, cells, groups of cells, animals with backbones and fins, animals with scales and giants in armor, animals with warm blood. The flowering of life and a burst of forms. Since the beginning perhaps five hundred million different species have appeared on earth.

And now the latest and most complex organization of cloud stuff known, man with his swollen brain. The human organization, the human pattern, is as unique compared to what has gone before as were the first living things in primeval seas. As new as a hatched chick or a baby. Another major beginning rooted in earlier beginnings but like none of them. Gravitation, magnetic fields, nuclear reactions and waves of light shape the stars and have helped to shape us. We are products of the very same forces that have given rise to a vast spectrum of things from interstellar dust clouds to satellites, from viruses to the highest apes. We share so much with everything else, and yet, for all that we share, we are radically different.

For better or for worse, we are a species on the make. We are evolving more rapidly than any other species which has ever existed. Even more significant, we are evolving along new lines. In us nature has produced a new order of restlessness that has been called everything from divine discontent and original sin to the workings of a cerebral driving mechanism. Whatever the source of the restlessness, it is an old and established tradition in our kind.

Our remote ancestors did not stop with making tools superior to ready-made natural implements. They kept on improving the improvements. They fought to get into the caves, and then left the caves to build shelters of their own. They found fire and dared to use it and then made it artificially. They were hunted and became hunters and developed strategy after strategy in the hunt. They transmuted their fear and their awe into spirits and demons.

Like them, we are inveterate disturbers of the peace, our own peace as well as the peace of all other living things. We are still strangers, newcomers, evolutionary zoot-suiters uneasy in an uneasy world, invaders and explorers and exploiters. To assist us in our restlessness we make tools and weapons and machines and instruments and symbols, enabling us to do things which our bodies are not designed to do directly. We are the first species with the power to build, self-consciously and deliberately, evolving accessories for our own evolution.

Accessories for evolution, devices to speed the shaping of

198

substance and the organization of matter and the creation of patterns conceived by minds. Machines reshape the earth and redistribute its materials. A bulldozer gouges its way toward a place between hills in the woods where a new home or a new factory or a new mine will be. The first step in reshaping—access, getting there. Roads open up the remnants of old wildernesses. Other giants follow the bulldozers, rumbling and clanking in along the gouges—mammoths with steel-girder necks and scoops to dig cellars and trenches, drills to probe for water, armor plates like the cowcatchers of old locomotives to push tree trunks and boulders out of the way.

Machines go after metals for more machines and fuels to keep the machines running. Power shovels take tons of ore at a single bite. Rock crushers and rock drillers and rock haulers move underground for coal and oil and the uranium of nuclear furnaces and nuclear weapons. Machines go to work on the raw materials. A man in a "pulpit," an enclosed control room in a steel plant, moves levers which adjust speeds and pressures, and watches down below where a red-hot plate passes through high-speed rollers and is squeezed into a long, thin strip. Other machines in other plants force plastics like spaghetti through holes and into molds, twist pretzels and shape loaves of bread, turn out foamy sheets of raw synthetic rubber.

There are machines that make machines—metal punches and cutters, rolling mills with gears fifteen feet across, forging presses fastened by bolts as big as fire hydrants to the floors of foundries the size of a football field. Automatic lathes, members of a new breed of power tools, have only to be "told" what to do. Their instructions are patterns of holes in moving tapes, each tape representing the design of a different part. These robots carve patterns to close engineering tolerances out of chunks of metal. Shaping machines, the brawn and muscle of a mechanical world.

199

A different class or order of devices includes the gatherers of raw data, undigested information. Instruments may keep track of events which lie beyond the limits of our senses. Sounds too faint to hear, the footfalls of an ant scuttling on a blade of grass and the jostling of unresting atomic particles, are detected by microphones and amplified and become as loud as the breaking of surf.

Sights too faint to see make their patterns on silver-grain emulsions, imprint themselves on photographic plates. Light from all corners of the observable universe, from the highest attics and subcellars of space, reaches our telescopes and the invisible becomes visible. We see stars and nebulae and jets of gas which the eye unaided cannot see. We see the collision of two spiral galaxies, two Milky Ways with stars and planets, probably some populated planets.

Instruments not only extend our natural senses, but create new ones. They reveal worlds of sensation which would otherwise be closed to us. Although we are not designed to detect radio waves, for example, that does not prevent us from viewing things with "radio eyes." There are objects in space which emit so little light that even our most powerful telescopes cannot detect them. But they also emit radio waves, and we tune in on the broadcasts with special aerials and receivers and map a universe of unseen radio stars.

Information is something which we may increase indefinitely, something which seems to grow without limit. We go after information intensively, voraciously, almost ferociously, as if we were starving for it. We store information and consume it as if it were a food without which the brain would wither. Legions and armies of instruments in the world's laboratories, and new laboratories being built, and new legions and armies of instruments. The instruments are everywhere, measuring and recording everything. The behavior of atoms and parts of atoms, the life courses of galaxies and stars, crystal structures, chemical reactions in healthy and diseased cells, wind velocities and currents undersea, cosmic rays, tremors beneath the earth's surface—the ceaseless electrical rhythms of the brain itself.

We set up the experimental conditions under which the instruments may operate. Many of them run automatically, twenty-four hours a day, unattended. Their records are charts and graphs and tabulations. Their records are information, and they furnish more information in a week than the instruments of half a century ago furnished in years or decades. Think of them as machines piling up masses of information the way bulldozers pile up masses of earth, turning out facts the way high-speed rolling mills turn out strips of steel, grinding out data to be used in the design of new machines and new theories.

We do not move through history alone. We go accompanied and surrounded on all sides by constellations of things of our own making. As long as we endure these things will be with us. They evolve with us. They are our evolution. Our machines are species of a sort, domesticated species not alive in themselves but alive because of us. They evolve according to specific laws, and some of the laws resemble closely those which govern the evolution of living things. Their development involves mutations, trial and error, successes and failures, weeding-outs, extinctions. They have their genealogies and elaborately branching family trees.

Change generally comes step by step among machines as among organisms. A group of engineers spends months modifying the shape of one part of a food-processing machine containing more than three thousand parts, a single cam. The new cam looks the same as the old one. The difference in curvature is so small that the eye cannot detect it, but now the machine vibrates far less at high speeds. A tiny change, a mutation which only experts can appreciate—experts, and the company's salesmen. The improved machine appears on the market and begins to outsell competing machines which

201

do the same job, only not quite so well. For a time it is the best and most successful model available, until other machines appear with other improvements, and the process of successive refinements and obsolescences continues.

Multiply this example a million times in all areas of applied science, in the making of aircraft engines and automatic harvesters and drugs to combat disease. New products in any industry are new varieties and new species, and the old exists together with the new. People still use ox carts and wooden ploughs and remedies concocted in the days of witchcraft. Sometimes, in some places, obsolescence is swift. A victrola with a crank for hand-winding and a hearing-trumpet loudspeaker, a radio set studded with a dozen dials and about the size of an orange crate, a touring car with high running boards and detachable side flaps to keep the rain out—these items bring high prices. They have become old-fashioned, antiques, in a generation or two. Industrial museums are filled with fossil devices, the giant insects and feathered lizards and dinosaurs of a past world of extinct machines.

There are also things of another sort which appear in increasingly complex patterns, evolve with us and our works, and are subject to laws of mutation and natural selection. The invention of words and other symbols is part of the same kind of evolution that has resulted in the invention of machines. Language, communication in all its forms, changes in the same way that living creatures change. Every novelty brings new words and new vocabularies. Whatever it is, a new device or a new kind of music or a new scientific theory, language expands and evolves with it.

Every year thousands of words are coined to name newly synthesized chemicals, newly built apparatus, newly discovered phenomena. Rates of word invention and word evolution vary widely. In the dead-end areas of science and in areas where we learn at a relatively sluggish pace new words come slowly, and investigators use vocabularies that differ little from vocabularies used in the past. But in other areas language throws out many roots and branches. The coining of words proceeds most actively in areas where we are exploring and learning most actively. Then new words spill out in showers like sparks from the edge of a blade being ground sharp.

For example, we are just beginning to study ourselves scientifically. We are just beginning to glimpse the shape of laws involving the behavior of people in groups, to understand the nature of communication and the meaning behind such general terms as "leadership" and "effective organization." Social scientists are inventing many words and so are investigators in genetics, biochemistry, nuclear physics and electronics. Some current lines of investigation will be extremely fruitful, and in them language will evolve and branch out richly in new directions.

Other work is likely to be less enlightening. It is based on crude and unwieldy concepts and gives rise to sheer jargon of the worst sort, ponderous and pretentious vocabularies which obscure more than they clarify, unwieldy dinosaur words. Such words, and the studies and notions from which they have emerged, will become extinct in a weeding-out process as ruthless and indispensable as natural selection.

In many cases even the best of words are too cumbersome to use. To express abstract concepts or relationships with the highest possible degree of precision, we must turn to mathematical symbols. Such symbols represent a shorthand for certain kinds of ideas, and in theory those ideas could be put into words. We can express an algebraic equation as "$X^3/2 + 3 = 7$" or "the sum of half the cube of an unknown number and three is equal to seven." For simple equations of this sort symbols may not appear to have any great advantage over words. But if we used words to express somewhat more involved equations, problems still within the realm of elementary algebra, the result might run to several paragraphs and be as difficult to read as a legal document.

Problems still more complex by a few orders of magnitude could never be expressed or solved or even conceived without the proper symbols. Such were the obstacles that confronted people of earlier times. There is no reason to believe that Egyptian mathematicians who lived some four thousand years ago were any less gifted than modern mathematicians. But as far as solving equations is concerned, they were dragging their way through mud. They had not developed the concepts or the symbols needed to approach problems which later generations would handle easily.

To be sure, they managed to struggle through certain simple algebraic equations without modern symbols. But it required a prodigious amount of effort. It was something like building pyramids without modern tools. Solving more sophisticated problems in those days would have been as hopeless as trying to erect an Empire State Building or a Golden Gate Bridge using only hammers, saws and monkey wrenches. Evolving mathematical symbols are tools for the building of the most abstract of abstract ideas. Aided by such tools a high-school student of average intelligence today routinely solves problems far beyond the powers of the most brilliant mathematicians of ancient Egypt.

Mathematics put to use is one example of the abstract in action, the power of symbols. We have symbols for abstractions, for the common elements relating things that may seem to have nothing in common. The sun and moon, twins, a shout and its echo, stones struck together to make fire —two heavenly bodies, two infants, two sounds, two stones. When man recognized that such things share the quality of "twoness," the notion of numbers was born. Similar insights gave rise to the notion of abstract geometrical form—a tree, a wheel, a limestone column in a cave, all have the shape of a cylinder.

The first abstractions, like the first cells on earth, were relatively simple. But they have evolved in a spectacular fashion, and things have been getting more and more complicated ever since. Today's abstractions are highly advanced species of ideas. They compare with the abstractions of yesterday as a man compares with a bacterium, or as the human brain compares with the crude nerve network of the sea anemone.

Today's most advanced abstractions find expression in mathematical equations. They have an enormously wide scope, covering basic relationships which underlie a host of phenomena. For example, so-called nonlinear differential equations are used in predicting weather and economic trends, plotting the orbits of satellites (natural and man-made), designing supersonic jet planes and missiles and nuclear power plants, studying the patterns of electrical pathways in the brain, and many other areas of modern research.

The calculations required to analyze these problems involve millions of steps. Each step may be a simple bit of arithmetic, an addition or subtraction or multiplication or division. But the task of undertaking all the necessary steps is too time-consuming for any single person, no matter how fast he can compute. It is even too much for teams of technicians equipped with ordinary desk calculating machines. So we build electronic calculators to do our mental bulldozing for us. Some of them compute several million times faster than the human brain. A team of a thousand men using pencil and paper would have to work more than seven years to solve a problem which a high-speed electronic calculator solves in a day.

Such machines may have several hundred thousand parts; they represent the most elaborate devices ever made. Furthermore, as we develop more and more complex abstractions, they are being called on to perform more and more complex duties. Investigators are designing machines which translate from one language to another, decipher codes, and learn from experience. A rapidly expanding branch of mathematics deals with strategies in warfare and business. Its equations express fundamental similarities among the activities of competing armies, competing companies—and competing chess and poker players. This is why current research on chess-playing machines, robot strategists, is of intense practical interest to industrial and military agencies.

The rise of new species and varieties of calculators. Accessories for the brain in the same sense that power tools are accessories for the muscles. They help us to handle the new species and varieties of abstractions which continually come into being in the world of ideas. Ideas evolve and compete with one another, and some dominate and some disappear. We no longer believe that the earth lies at the center of the universe, or that living things are born spontaneously out of mud and fermenting grain, or that the stars are lights shining through holes in the sky.

Extinct museum beliefs, fossil ideas imprinted on the pages of old books. Ideas that have changed bit by bit until they bear little resemblance to what they were. Changing images of atoms. The first atoms were thought to be particles with hooks and rounded or jagged edges. Since then they have been a great many things, including solid billiard-ball bodies, electrons imbedded in a positively charged substance like raisins in jelly, submicroscopic solar systems consisting of nuclei with planetary electrons. Today's atoms are electron clouds surrounding complex nuclei shaped like drops of water. A picture gallery of fundamental particles as conceived at different times in different places by different minds. Democracy was one thing to the Greeks and other things to other peoples. It has undergone strange mutations in our times.

Some ideas seem not to change over the centuries. In this respect they resemble some living species. Sphenodon, a lizardlike creature, is almost a dead ringer for its ancestors which lived 135,000,000 years ago. The oyster and horseshoe crab have remained pretty much the same for about two hundred million years, while one type of sea shell has endured twice as long without notable alterations. Ideas may also suffer relatively little change in a changing world. Great, hardy ideas like those embodied in the Ten Commandments—and lesser ideas like those of the vegetarians and flat-worlders and astrologers.

But the general rule is evolution everywhere. Increasing complexity in everything, as each generation builds on the achievements of preceding generations and uses their discoveries and innovations. Evolution in physical feats. A man gets an idea and does something about it, and inevitably other men imitate him and then go him one better, and sooner or later they too are surpassed. Pioneers become has-beens.

Once it was enough for a tightrope walker to go high above crowds, holding a long pole for balance and hesitating and teetering as the crowds gasped. Now to earn applause and a living he must set a chair on the tightrope and stand on the chair and work a hula hoop and juggle five balls, all at the same time. Once acrobats on ice skates jumped over half a dozen barrels in a row. Now they go somersaulting, heels over head, across fifteen to twenty barrels. Goals of the past: the fifteen-foot pole vault, the seven-foot high jump, the four-minute mile.

Evolution in the arts. There is no challenge in doing things that have been done superbly before. Furthermore, we could not do them if we would. Times change and our feelings and ways of expression change, so that we have no choice but to shape new forms and new patterns. Compare a Gregorian chant with a composition by Stravinsky, a medieval ballad with a poem like "The Waste Land," a Renaissance painting with a painting by Klee. The differences have nothing to do with better or worse, with degrees of greatness or creativity. It is a matter of evolution. All arts, like all concepts and works in mathematics or science, are increasing in refinement and subtlety and complexity. In all fields of experience and endeavor there are virtuosos, avant-gardists, among us.

We keep tampering with things, making and breaking and remaking traditions. We are unique for our continual experimenting. What other animals do depends almost entirely on their inherited genes. Like single-purpose machines, they may be marvelously designed to achieve their goals, but they cannot change their workings or create new goals for themselves. They have little to do with their own evolution. They are passive creatures in the sense that nature works on them through the laws of organic change. If mutation stopped among all the other two million species existing on earth, they would eventually cease evolving. If mutation stopped in us, we could continue to evolve indefinitely, swiftly and along lines that no one can foresee.

Our genes, like the genes of other animals, cannot be "taught." They do not change as a direct result of what we learn. They have gone on reproducing themselves in the same old ways with the same old accuracy. Their basic workings have remained unaffected by all the knowledge we have accumulated, by all the theories and machines and traditions which have come and gone during the past. But our genes shape the hands and brains that make it possible for us to evolve independently of them to an extent, to evolve extra-genetically or culturally.

Other animals convey some of their memories, something of what they have learned, to their offspring. But among them there is no such thing as accumulating knowledge in the human sense. Although the young may learn, learning has to be done all over again in the second generation—and over and over again in succeeding generations. It is like filling a cup with a hole in it. You have to pour and keep pouring so that the water level will stay the same. Furthermore, it is impossible for any living thing to communicate all that it has learned. Animals communicate only a small fraction of what they acquire by experience.

A good deal more can be accomplished in us. The specific skills and knowledge we gain during our lifetimes cannot produce mutations in any of our genes, much less favorable mutations in the specific genes involved in forming the brain. But we pass things from generation to generation outside our genes. We may inherit by education.

Like animals, we cannot communicate all we know. Some things die with us. A skilled worker, a lens grinder or airplane designer, can teach apprentices just so much of his craft and no more. A master chess player can analyze and describe many details of the strategies he has worked out in many matches. But he cannot always tell exactly why he makes certain moves in new and unusual circumstances. Under such conditions he relies on his intuition, a kind of "feel," and that cannot be conveyed.

So there are things which remain unexpressed and nevertheless influence our actions. There are also expressed things which, wisely or unwisely, other people may not heed. These include the warnings of elder statesmen, the insights of critics, the advice of parents to children. Still, with all our communication problems, we learn and convey considerably more than the highest animals. They lose more knowledge than they transmit, while we transmit more than we lose.

Marks of the latest, and probably not the last, great breakthrough in the evolution of matter. It is like the start of a brilliant play in a football game. For a few seconds we are confused. There are pile-ups and spins and fakes and feints, and players move in different directions. A whole complex of tricks and distractions. But the real action is taking place near the center, among a tangled mass of blockers and would-be tacklers, where everything seems to be hopelessly jammed. Suddenly it is a jam no longer. The ball carrier breaks loose. He is in the clear, away for a long dash, dodging and picking up blockers as he goes. It is the beginning of an open-field run.

We are at a similar stage as a species, although the analogy is obviously not complete. We are running in the open, but, like recently freed animals, we are still confused with our freedom. We are recent apes rushing in many directions and rushing so impetuously that there is always a danger of falling flat on our faces. For example, our instruments and meters record information almost too swiftly. An automatic instrument at one astronomical observatory tracks meteors so efficiently that if investigators allowed it to operate continuously for a single month, it would gather enough information to keep them busy for three years. So the machine runs for a few days or a week and is then switched off while they catch up.

It is the same in many laboratories. Fortunately, our instruments can be shut down, or else we would soon be inundated in a Sorcerer's Apprentice flood of information. Things are complicated enough as it is. Scientists generally publish less than a third of their experimental findings, but that still represents an appalling amount of data. As a conservative estimate, the world's scientific journals publish more than a million and a half articles a year, which averages out to about 170 articles an hour. Our total knowledge, the number of facts we gather in our research, is doubling every fifteen years or so.

The human brain is growing invisibly. It does not grow in substance but in information. It does not retain all the information. Even its voluminous storehouses of memory are much too limited for that. Its overflowing experiences are housed in accessory memories, in volumes and microfilms, in libraries and museums and archives, in the growing electronic

HUMAN PREHISTORY

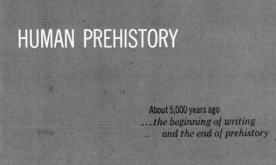

About 5,000 years ago
...*the beginning of writing
and the end of prehistory*

...e early stone tools...

About 10,000 years ago
...*we are on the verge
of leaving the caves*

About 50,000 years ago
...*modern-type men
begin to dominate*

150,000 to 35,000 years ago
...*Neanderthal big-game hunters*

750,000 to 500,000 years ago
...*man uses fire and enters caves*

memories of more and more computing machines. Knowledge continues to increase faster and faster.

At times it seems like a nightmare. Little details accumulate, things to be done—homework or household chores or memos and reports. Nightmares of lengthening lists and things forgotten, and lost tickets and baggage and missed trains, and overwhelming confusion and never reaching home. Learning may have a nightmare quality in our most harried moments. We may fear and resent it. But it persists. It is the brain's fault. Nothing, not even illusion or faith, can distract us forever from the buzzing, stinging insistence of a contradiction or of a fact that has not yet found its place. This is a sign that we are on the move.

Our kind of evolution is a permanent and self-feeding dissatisfaction. Nature's way is not good enough for us. A leading biologist has said: "Natural selection has no foresight. It is opportunistic. Man has committed himself to questioning the wisdom of nature and to following his own wisdom, big or small, in place of hers." There is something cold and hard-boiled and almost mechanical at the core of natural selection. Stripped of all alleviating verbiage, it is essentially devil-take-the-hindmost.

If an animal has the "wrong" genes, it is doomed. Its genes may be wrong from an evolutionary standpoint. That is, it may be perfectly healthy but unfit to cope with a changing environment. Eohippus, the dawn horse, had no trouble until things became cooler and drier. Then it found more and more tough grasses, and fewer and fewer tender leaves and shoots. It was trapped by circumstances, and became extinct. Weeding out may proceed on an individual as well as a species basis, involving animals born sickly or deformed. There are short-term as well as long-term exterminations.

In either case, the result is unavoidable. The great majority of animals and species vanish. Death is the standard weapon for weeding out. No animal, no animal society, can help its young to overcome or compensate for their genes. If a cub is lame or a nestling unable to fly, nothing will save it. Parents can do nothing about it. Instincts are futile. This is how the old original evolution works, and it works unchallenged in all species but one.

We fight back. For thousands of centuries the fighting back was puny and futile. Men propitiated or exorcised demons and still succumbed to epidemics. Diseases swept through entire populations, sparing individuals who happened to be resistant and striking down the rest. Survivors comforted and consoled those that were dying. Spectators at deathbeds. Plagues came as mysteriously and inexorably as fate. Indeed, the notion of fate may have arisen in the minds of prehistoric men who watched in fear and trembling the march of disease, and tried cures and failed. Fate is another word for natural selection.

We learn, and the status of fate falls somewhat. We cure and prevent many infectious diseases. We save the lives of people born with genes that play a role in diabetes, pernicious anemia and other conditions. The old evolution still works in us. It might even "solve" some of our most urgent research problems. In the natural course of things, for example, cancer might cease to be the killer it is. If we were still spectators at deathbeds and still exorcised demons, time might come to our rescue. After thousands of generations and billions upon billions of deaths, it is possible that breeds of cancer-resistant men and women would arise.

That is nature's way, not ours. It can never be ours, and we are having none of it. In the old evolution individuals are important only to further the cause of the species, as means to an end. If individuals mean more to many of us, if death matters, it is because we are something new under the sun. We have the power and will to care, to fight back. The notion that a life may be worth saving is nonsense in terms of the

212

old evolution, but everything in terms of human evolution. The coming of man has changed the meaning, and is changing the nature, of life and death.

Evolution shows no signs of slacking off. In fact, more species probably exist than have existed at any previous time. The earth is more abundant and crowded and complicated than ever before. Species are forming and dying out today as they have been for perhaps three billion years. But in the midst of it all we are the outstanding innovation, and we are evolving at an unprecedented rate. The symbol of our development—a rocket at a launching site and a count-down. A roar and smoke and flame. For the briefest instant inertia, no motion, and when the motion starts it is very slow. The rocket rises a little way, perpendicular and ponderous, as if it would never leave the ground.

We are at the very beginning of the climb. The rocket is still perpendicular, but moves faster now with a jet-wake of fire. The future? A dud perhaps, and a broken plunge. Or an arcing up and away, and speed mounting like the sound of a siren, and at last the sudden spurt, as if the rocket is being sucked up and up into space, beyond the moon and toward the stars. Possibilities that concern us, for we are not spectators. We have helped make this rocket and we are in it. Our future is a flight involving such things as targets and destinations.

Futures

in Space

13

WE exist in an enormous near-nothingness, a universe which just barely falls short of being completely empty. Take the volume of the known universe. Out of ten billion billion billion parts of space only one part is occupied by matter. An almost negligible trace, and most of it goes into the making of stars and gas clouds.

The rest, a trace of a trace, is used for everything else. Our earth represents an even smaller fraction of this available fraction and consists chiefly of inanimate matter, seas and rocks and molten core. Only one ten-trillionth of its substance is shaped into living things. And of all living things on earth human beings make up another fraction. We are a superdistillate of the inconceivably sparse stuff of the universe, a swiftly evolving superdistillate with a new kind of future. Eons of cosmic evolution lie behind us—a hundred million centuries before Christ, less than twenty centuries after.

What lies ahead is not entirely obscure. Indeed, we know

214

parts of our future far better than we know parts of our past. Things are changing swiftly, so swiftly that even the future is not what it used to be. Once as remote as the mountains of the moon, it looms before us all of a sudden. We are catching up fast with what was imagination in yesterday's science fiction. It is already abundantly clear that the next great burst of complexity, the next great push, will carry us into space and closer to the stars.

The future has already become a pressing, tangible thing. We feel its presence and its mounting needs in many ways. Would-be balancers of national budgets, for example, must contend with items which would have appeared far-fetched five or ten years ago. These items spell out in dollars and cents the costs of preliminary blueprints and models and plans specifying the tactics and strategies of space travel— salaries, contracts, schedules, legalities, deadlines, a growing mass of detail.

A report of the President's Science Advisory Committee suggests that our first delegates to space may not be human. As a start it might be wiser to send "remotely controlled scientific expeditions to the moon and nearby planets." Research is under way on mechanical scouts, tanks that will move out of rocket ships on treads and be guided by radio waves from earth. Robots may run the first risks and roll across alien landscapes in the tanks, reporting back what they find. They will be expendable. If they run out of fuel or break down, we can abandon them without regrets.

Another report recognizes what we all know deep down. Man will follow his robots into space, assuming he can wait that long. "There may be a point at which the complexity of the machine to do the job becomes intolerable and at which a man is found to be more efficient, more reliable, and above all more resourceful when unexpected obstacles arise. It is, in a sense, an article of faith that man will indeed be required to do the job of cosmic exploration personally—and, furthermore, that he will *want* to do the job himself, whether required to or not."

So investigators work on the complex problems and paraphernalia of manned flight. They are designing satellite launching sites which will be assembled in space and serve, among other things, as possible take-off platforms for exploring rockets. They are testing materials to protect rockets against meteor impacts, and to protect crew members against the effects of cosmic rays. Special exercises are being devised for muscles gone flaccid during gravity-free flight. There must be special ways of combatting the emotional stresses of flying for long periods through the isolation and silences of space.

Calculations. About 1,500,000 pounds of thrust are required to send a man to the moon and get him back again. A radio system with a power of about two hundred kilowatts will keep earthbound observers in touch with their colleagues on Mars. Schedules. According to one plan, the first step will be space flights lasting a week to a month, satellites orbiting around the earth and the moon, and containing a maximum of three persons each. Then longer flights, round trips to Mars and Venus lasting two to three years, crews of three to five persons. Finally, the beginnings of a breed of men and women who will choose space as a way of life.

Measuring by the time scale of the universe, in which a million years is equivalent to a second or two for us, all this will happen in a flash. Among investigators actively engaged in space research, those closest to the accelerating pace of events, there are staunch conservatives. They believe that advanced forms of space travel will be a reality within two centuries. The radicals are impatient with such statements, which they regard as products of extreme overcautiousness. One of them tells an audience casually: "I feel certain that many of you in this hall today will have grandchildren who will not be born on earth."

Sooner or later, but in any case, not long as evolution is measured. Research continues, budgets rise, and many things are imminent. Imagine an observer watching us from the skies. He must guess at what we are doing. We appear to him as objects seen from the top of an immense skyscraper, as little black moving dots. Considerable activity occurs among the clumps, where the dots are thickest. Patterns form like crystals, singly and in clusters. Rectangular structures take shape, toy-block structures, artificial caves of a sort, with holes in them. The dots stream in and out at regular intervals, rhythmically. The dots come and go in metal shells that glitter in the sun, along black and white strips which intersect and branch off and twist into cloverleaf formations.

Everything takes place on the thin, crinkled crust of the planet, or almost everything. Every now and then, at points located away from the clumps and the strips, there is a flash and a puff of smoke. The biggest puffs produce nothing visible. But out of the tops of some puffs rise new types of metal shells, dart-shaped shells like seeds ejected from white flowers or rocks from the mouths of volcanoes. Most of these shells fall back toward the earth. A few stay up and go in orbits for a time. In a little while our observer will see a great many of them.

After half a million years of clinging to a crust, we are preparing to invade space. Our feet are still on the ground, but we look at the skies appraisingly, weighing chances and risks. This sort of thing has happened before. Other navigators must have felt the way we feel as they stood on shore and looked at unfamiliar seas and planned voyages. Some of them ventured a little way and came back with eye-witness reports of places where the ocean spilled in waterfalls over the edges of a flat world, waves rising steep as the slopes of mountains, dragons larger than ships.

Our imagination is less vivid. Little green men flying in saucers represent the best we have done so far. There is no

217

telling what tall tales the future may bring. Dragons may yet appear in our skies, aerial Loch Ness monsters. But they will not stop us any more than they stopped the first ocean voyagers—or the prehistoric men who began breaking with age-old traditions some ten thousand years ago and moved their firesides a little way out of the caves. We are also moving out into the open, into new and wider places. In a sense we are also leaving caves. In a sense, we will always be leaving caves.

Judging by events of the long past, the sweep of patterns from galaxies on, the drive toward space is currently the central fact of human existence. It has the feel of evolution about it, the old feel of restlessness and novelty and the beginning of a breakthrough. The new voyages that lie ahead represent an imminent spread of terrestrial life, the occupation of niches beyond our planet. The unique thing is that they are coming so swiftly and that their coming is deliberate.

A new and complex variable has entered the evolutionary equation, human purpose. As far as remote prehuman times are concerned, we may argue and argue. We have heard people state as if they knew for certain that the universe is a huge accident, a thing as random and meaningless as the shaping and dispersal of clouds. We have heard other people state with equal conviction that it is all the result of a master plan which unfolds like the plot of a novel. Purpose or no purpose. You may take your choice, on faith. Do not look for proof. This debate cannot be resolved. Neither rhetoric nor scientific evidence has anything to contribute to it.

But there is a difference before and after the coming of man. Every fact, every law, of evolution demonstrates and italicizes the uniqueness of human purpose, the existence in us of goals that change as we change the world. A new and higher order of purpose. We plan decades ahead, and we could plan for the next century or the next millennium. As the only species with evolving purposes, we have responsibilities and potentialities. Whether or not we realize those potentialities is another question. Here again there are debates and we must in the last analysis go on faith. Here there is a variety of conceivable futures and some offer mankind little hope. They need not come to pass, but they could if we refused to recognize dangers ahead.

For one thing, the possibility of extinction cannot be ruled out. It could happen in a number of ways. Another world war could destroy us, even if we failed to wipe ourselves out with nuclear weapons. We could lose our will to explore and learn and plan, our unique and fragile capacity for caring. Shortly before he died Einstein was asked whether he would enter the same profession if he had the chance to relive his life. There was bitterness and discouragement in his answer: "I would rather choose to be a plumber or a peddler in the hope to find that modest degree of independence still available under present circumstances."

Other investigators express similar feelings, usually in private. Two world wars have done sufficient damage to the human spirit. A third could create a "beat species" rather than merely a "beat generation." It could leave us as empty of aspiration as a child who has been rejected many times and lives now without hope or self-respect or the expectation of love. For a species in such a state, extinction would amount to mercy killing.

It is abundantly evident that the end might come with mass killings made possible by megaton hydrogen bombs. From one standpoint we would deserve it. It would be grim justice, a punishment for the crime of Cain, for our subsavage aggressiveness and brutality. After all, part of us is beast. But this misses the point, the full complexity of the human situation. Crisis is built into us and our existence. Everything we do, whether for good or for evil, leads us headlong into emergencies. We are always plunging toward destruction, teetering on edges.

219

Suppose that we had never invented nuclear weapons or weapons of any sort. Suppose we were filled to the brim with humanity and felt only love for our fellow men. Nevertheless, with the best intentions in the world we would still find ourselves up against a variety of possible catastrophes. That is how things actually stand today. Love is not enough. Those who cry "Get out of here and love one another!" are desperate, and desperation is not enough either.

With or without nuclear wars, we still face the threat of extinction from another direction—and in this case it has nothing at all to do with the evil in us. The threat rises out of the other side of our nature, the human side. There is no obvious justice in it, but we face catastrophe because we refuse to meet death passively, because we keep saving and prolonging lives.

Our successful fight against disease runs directly counter to the laws of the old evolution. It has upset the balance of things. Before us nature had her own effective way of taking care of the less fit and the unfit. The weak and sickly and handicapped of other species were left to die and be devoured. We have discarded this way of doing things, the way of natural selection, and have chosen not to rely completely on death. The brakes are off. If multiplying is any criterion for a successful species, we are highly successful. We are in the process of flooding the earth with our numbers.

Change, evolution, may be as distressing as disease. Bigger and better traffic jams, more hectic rush hours, apartments becoming slums so fast that new housing lags behind, not enough teachers and too many pupils. These are only a few symptoms of our spreading. Farms and woodlands sold for Levittowns, lawyers coming in with zoning laws and pages of fine print, suburbs creeping out from the cities and touching the suburbs of other cities. Places we knew as children, places we found near shores and lakes and rock, turned to picnic grounds. Empty beer cans among pools and leaves.

220

The situation is bad enough right now, and it will be much worse. Imagine the crowds and the Levittowns doubling or tripling everywhere. By the most conservative estimates the world's population will nearly double within the next century. It will rise to at least five billion persons, and many authorities consider seven billion a more likely figure. It is difficult to conceive what this will mean in terms of worldwide unrest, migration pressures, food shortages, and possible famines—that is, if nothing radical is done about it and done soon.

Saving lives is a dangerous business in more ways than one. It can promote a decline in the quality of rising populations. We face a serious crisis involving the quality of our genes, and it is all the fault of the doctors. Every time a doctor successfully treats a patient suffering from one of the many conditions in which heredity may play an important part, such as diabetes or epilepsy or schizophrenia, he is helping to preserve unfavorable genes which will spread like an epidemic among future populations. Every time a surgeon repairs the tissues of a baby born with a major heart defect, he is doing his bit to frustrate the natural law of weeding out the least fit.

Systematically and with malice aforethought, we are safeguarding genes capable of producing the same diseases for doctors to treat in times yet to come. It is like a national debt, the paying of which may be postponed and postponed—but sooner or later future generations will have to pay. The number of unfavorable genes increases as medicine advances and we cure recently incurable diseases. At present the average person has about thirty to forty thousand genes. This total includes certain potentially dangerous genes, each of which would bring on a different disease if it were transmitted under the proper circumstances. Fortunately, such genes are not sufficiently potent by themselves to exert their full effects. That happens only when persons with the same bad genes

221

happen to mate and pass a double dose of unfavorable heredity to their children.

But we do not carry these genes lightly. They are not entirely suppressed. Each of them contributes a small but definitely harmful effect. It may be expressed as recurring headaches, attacks of arthritis, eye trouble, or any one of a dozen symptoms. We may be afflicted somewhat earlier with tremors, loss of memory, bouts of bad temper and depression and remorse. Such conditions may represent the workings of recessive genes acting partially, as it were. The result is that life expectancy and the ability to reproduce may be lowered by twenty percent or more. Without our burden of recessive genes, for example, the average length of life would now be about eighty-five years.

One further word about longevity. It is, in a sense, our own invention. As far as the old evolution is concerned, it does not matter how long the individuals of any species live— provided they live through the period when they can mate and breed. After that, they are of no use. They are pods to be discarded once the genes inside them have been passed along. Living beyond the age of reproduction becomes meaningful only in our scheme of things, in our kind of evolution.

So medical investigators continue to seek improved treatments, particularly for illnesses most common after the age of fifty. No doctor doubts that research will lead to the discovery of new ways of combatting cancer, heart disease and other conditions which baffle us now. We shall continue to preserve and hoard bad genes. New mutants will arise, because DNA molecules do not reproduce themselves perfectly. New diseases will come as we curb the old ones. At least one person in five carries a detrimental gene which his parents did not have.

Furthermore, we have decided to run the risk of increasing our natural mutation rates. We are producing and using a variety of radiations. Selected patients are exposed to x-rays in hospitals and doctors' offices. All of us are exposed to radio-active fall-out from the testing of nuclear weapons. In a misguided effort to allay anxieties semantically, the term "sunshine unit" has been invented to measure the doses we are receiving. The term has a warm and cheery sound. But it would be difficult to conceive of a more insensitive and degrading abuse of language. No tasteless trick can conceal the fact that genetic damage done today can leave scars on children yet to be born.

No matter how far or how fast medicine advances, by itself it represents a losing fight against our accumulating load of mutations. New treatments alone cannot prevent us from ending up as a moribund breed, a population of pale, sickly creatures lingering on with the aid of pills and injections and surgery and electronic devices to bolster our fading senses. If we continue to do as we are doing, even our drive to learn and act will decline with the decline of intelligence and the unbraked rise of populations.

This by no means exhausts the list of unattractive futures. For instance, staying put could be as grim as declining. Other species have lived gloriously through and past their heydays, developing relatively rapidly, then reaching a plateau and remaining very much the same for tens of millions or hundreds of millions of years.

It has been observed that the combination of a man and a machine tends to behave more like a machine than a man. A hint of what we may become? We could attain a terrible half-robot existence, a kind of automatic and thoughtless social system in which the individual is brainwashed beyond recognition as a human being. This is the recurrent theme of *Land Under England, Brave New World, 1984* and other visions of stagnation.

Nowadays predictions concerning the future of man are usually on the gloomy side. Naïve optimism does not rate as high as it did during the times of the Victorians and their em-

223

pires, or even after the First World War. We have come through so much. We have been the prey of other animals, and fought for the caves with weapons and fire. We have survived ice ages and dark ages, and seen a succession of brave new renaissances. Yet we no longer seem so sure that we can work things out. Naïve pessimism is more fashionable, or at least it is better publicized. It has gone literary, and there is much to read about the inevitable decline of human society.

Most of these forebodings belittle man. They assume that we will or can do nothing about anything, when our entire history is a record of getting into and out of apparent impasses. Perhaps we will not wipe ourselves out. We can manage to feed and control the size of our rising population. We can do something more than select in a negative way, something more than merely save the lives of people with unfavorable genes. The fact that we value the life of the individual is forcing us into a position where positive selection becomes a prerequisite for the survival of the species. It is conceivable that we will select increasingly for the conditions and genes which favor intelligence, emotional stability, curiosity, social feeling, imagination.

Prophets of doom are not discouraged by the possibility of human survival. There is always the chance of stagnation. If man does not go under, he may cease to evolve. He may regiment himself into a rigid system like that of the ant or other social insects. Of course, arguments exist on the other side, too, although we hear less of them. We hear little about the forces which are tending to create new patterns of life, to produce greater and greater variety among us.

The world is becoming a melting pot of all breeds. The human beings of a thousand years from now will differ more widely from one another than we do. There will be more short and more tall people, more people with skins of in-between shades which are not yellow or black or white. There will be more combinations of features—blond hair with dark skin, almond-shaped eyes with large stocky bodies, Roman noses on negroid faces. And together with physical variety will come new combinations of psychological and temperamental traits. Genetics provides little evidence for the regimentation of the species.

The world of the ant is no model for us. It includes queens, workers and soldiers marching in long well-organized columns. Some colonies have "farms" and cultivate their own plants, or domesticate other insects. Ant hill societies are all the more impressive when you remember that they represent the work of an extremely elementary nervous system, one that contains only two or three hundred cells. The human brain is inconceivably more complex. It is made up of patterns involving ten thousand million nerve cells. To see ourselves in the image of the ant, even remotely, is a colossal failure of imagination.

If we do stagnate, it is not likely to be soon, and our ultimate patterns of behavior and society will differ enormously from the patterns of current times. We may crystallize into a rigid framework, and arrive at the end of doubt and learning, the end of history. We may achieve near-perfect stability and certainty and the absolute, and the only way to achieve such things is to stop evolving.

But by that time we will already have created new patterns and reshaped parts of the solar system for our own purposes. By that time floating bulldozers will have cleared away debris in the asteroid belt between Mars and Jupiter. We will have built floating cities and airports and observatories in the skies. Our super ant hills, if they ever come, will rise and reach out into space.

Another possibility—we may neither stagnate nor become extinct. We may be the first species to keep evolving. It is clear that all other species on earth are chiefly products of their genes. The fact that our prospects depend more and more on evolution outside our genes, on the human evolution of devices and symbols and ideas and ideals, may make the difference. Human evolution may proceed indefinitely. There is certainly no reason to ignore this possibility, even though it bears the stigma of hope.

In any case, our future is probably a very long one. We are just beginning to flex our muscles. All we have learned since our cave days has been a brief prelude to a step as significant as the invasion of the land by creatures ceasing to be fish. We are also ceasing to be something, and becoming something else. Satellites and planet-bound rockets are our flounderings in a new medium which is empty of life but will one day be populated. We are crawling toward new shorelines, into pools and mud flats at the edge of space.

From now on our evolution and the evolution of stars and galaxies will be more intimately bound. We, or the species that evolve from and surpass us, will move closer to events and processes with their own laws of development. The earth cannot house us forever. As a medium-sized yellow star, the sun is burning at a leisurely rate compared to that of fast-living members of the galaxy, the more massive blue stars. It has swelled a bit during its past five billion years, its equator having increased by more than 350,000 miles.

The sun has also been getting hotter. The temperature of our planet has risen about nine degrees Fahrenheit every billion years. If the sun keeps warming, and astronomers expect it to, our descendants will have difficulties. In two hundred and twenty million years, about the period from the first dinosaurs to the present day, the earth's temperature will climb another two degrees. This is enough to melt all the ice of the polar regions, raise the levels of the oceans, and submerge large coastal areas which include many of our major cities. Eventually it may be wise to move to another planet, further away from the sun.

Of course, that will be only postponing the need for more ambitious and remote migrations. At best the solar system will be livable for no more than six or seven billion years. As the sun exhausts its available hydrogen fuel, it will enter the red-giant stage and expand rapidly and become much hotter. Oceans will boil away. Rock will soften and melt and flow. Man-made things will become one great slag as dams and bridges and buildings melt with the rocks. Finally the sun is expected to collapse, cooling and fading and shrinking to about the size of the earth. Our planet will be locked in an eternal deep freeze as its temperature drops toward minus three hundred degrees below zero.

Long long before that, however, we may have gone elsewhere. There are adventures and surprises in store for us, and some of them could come much sooner than we expect. For example, the near future holds possibilities of learning about highly evolved forms of life outside the solar system. Our first contacts with species living on the satellites of other stars may not be the result of space trips and in-person visits.

We may detect signals from them in answer to our signals. Radio science has already advanced so far that electronic equipment which can transmit messages to the stars and receive messages from the stars may be developed within a decade or two. If that happens we shall have an intriguing job of decoding on our hands, and then there will be interstellar conversations. We may learn a good deal about the powers and ways of life of the beings that communicate with us, long before meeting them face to face.

And it takes little imagination to suggest that we shall meet them sooner or later. Nuclear energy is like a new kind of fire. It may free us for wider migrations, just as the old fire made it possible for early man to leave tropical places and invade colder wildernesses. Methods of reaching the stars have not yet passed the stage of vague speculation. But one Nobel Prize winner has expressed the feelings of many of his colleagues: "A visit to the stars is not imminent, but we may well be nearer to it in time than we are to Peking man."

One last look ahead, this time into infinity or near-infinity. Right now, for every star that dies three to four new ones are being born, condensing out of interstellar gases. If the supply of these gases is limited, if only a limited amount of material is available and no more, the Milky Way is doomed. In the long run, which may be thousands of billions of years, stellar death rates will equal and then exceed stellar birth rates. Eventually there will be no new births. Sterility and a cluster of cold dead white dwarfs.

Or another alternative. Recent research indicates the presence of wide gas streams near the center of the Milky Way, turbulent rivers rushing toward the outer rim of the galactic disc at speeds of a hundred miles a second or more. Apparently the rivers have been flowing for eons, and that raises problems. Our star system should long since have been drained of its gases, unless there is a "spring" which provides fresh gases to keep the rivers flowing. The source may be the corona or halo of thin gases which surrounds the galaxy and replenishes outward-streaming substance. The source itself may be replenished as the Milky Way moves through space and accumulates intergalactic matter in passing. Perhaps new raw material for new stars is entering the Milky Way continually.

Alternatives, too, for the future of the universe. One theory involves the perennial supply problem on a larger scale. If the total amount of matter in the universe is fixed, all stars and all galaxies everywhere will ultimately cool like the embers of a dying fire. The cosmos will become a great dead thing, a kind of extinct volcano. Or perhaps, as many investigators believe, this doomsday is a myth. Perhaps matter is being created all the time, and new stars and galaxies will form forever in a forever expanding universe. This is an infinite universe, always evolving and without beginning or end. It is not growing old but simply growing, which is something quite different.

We do not know enough to decide between these futures. The shadow of death over the universe, the unavoidable fate of pagan beliefs—or infinity. The proponents of doomsday could be right or wrong. But we see what has been transient in the scheme of things during times past, what shrinks and dies. It is not symmetry, not order, that is becoming less. In our portion of the universe at least, in the process from the original cloud to us, we see a steady decline of chaos. It is disorder which diminishes—and pattern that increases and grows. This is the fundamental reason for emphasizing always life over death, beginnings over endings.

We are a beginning. We are on the verge of carrying our kind of life, our genes and evolving patterns and traditions, into the new lands and new oceans of space. One day perhaps the earth will no longer be our dwelling place. We may exhaust its natural resources and leave it like an empty shell or a cocoon after the butterfly has flown. We may leave it hesitantly, as early men left their caves in the yellow-brown limestone cliffs of Palestine.

If so, we shall look back at the earth and preserve it as long as it lasts, as a memorial ground dedicated to vanished ancestors. A prehistoric site where ancient breeds fought and learned and launched their first interplanetary vessels. A deserted cave of a sort remembered for explorations and rituals practiced in dark places. A greater and even more meaningful Mount Carmel.

Selected Bibliography

General and Physical Sciences

Beck, Stanley D., *The Simplicity of Science.*
  Doubleday & Company, 1959.
Buchter, Julius, *Philosophical Writings of Peirce.*
  Dover Publications, 1955.
Gardner, Martin, *Fads and Fallacies in the Name of Science.*
  Dover Publications, 1955.
Hoyle, Fred, *Frontiers of Astronomy.*
  Harper & Brothers, 1955.
Kramer, Edna E., *The Main Stream of Mathematics.*
  Oxford University Press, 1951.
O'Neill, Joseph, *Land Under England.*
  Simon and Schuster, 1935.
Payne-Gaposchkin, Cecelia, *Stars in the Making.*
  Harvard University Press, 1952.
Singer, Charles, *A Short History of Science.*
  Oxford University Press, 1941.
Thomson, George, *The Foreseeable Future.*
  Cambridge University Press, 1955.

Biology and Evolution

Bates, Marston, and Humphrey, Philip S., *The Darwin Reader.*
  Charles Scribners Sons, 1956.
Bernal, J. D., *The Physical Basis of Life.*
  Routledge and Kegan Paul, 1951.
Dobzhansky, T., *Evolution, Genetics and Man.*
  John Wiley & Sons, 1955.

Eiseley, Loren, *The Immense Journey.*
  Random House, 1957.
Oparin, A. I., *The Origin of Life.*
  Dover Publications, 1953.
Rush, J. H., *The Dawn of Life.*
  Hanover House, 1957.
Schrödinger, E., *What Is Life?*
  Macmillan Company, 1946.
Sherrington, Charles, *Man On His Nature.*
  Macmillan Company, 1941.
Simpson, G. G., Pittendrigh, C. S., and Tiffany, L. H.,
  Life—An Introduction to Biology.
  Harcourt, Brace and Company, 1957.
Simpson, G. G., *The Meaning of Evolution.*
  Yale University Press, 1949.
Young, J. Z., *Doubt and Certainty In Science.*
  Oxford University Press, 1951.

Anthropology

Baumann, Hans, *The Caves of the Great Hunters.*
  Pantheon Books, 1954.
Braidwood, Robert J., *Prehistoric Men.*
  Chicago Natural History Museum, 1948.
Childe, Gordon V., *Man Makes Himself.*
  C. A. Watts & Company, 1936.
———, *What Happened In History.*
  Penguin Books, 1954.
Coon, Carleton S., *The Story of Man.*
  Alfred A. Knopf, 1955.
———, *The Seven Caves.*
  Alfred A. Knopf, 1957.
Eiseley, Loren, "Neanderthal Man and the Dawn of Human
  Paleontology." *Quarterly Review of Biology.* December, 1957.
Golding, William, *The Inheritors.*
  Faber and Faber Ltd., 1955.
Oakley, Kenneth P., "A Definition of Man."
  Science News, No. 20. Penguin Books, 1951.
Wendt, Herbert, *In Search of Adam.*
  Houghton Mifflin Company, 1956.
Wheeler, Mortimer, *Still Digging.*
  E. P. Dutton Company, 1956.

A B O U T   T H E   A U T H O R

JOHN PFEIFFER, one of the foremost American writers on science, is concerned primarily with presenting a broad picture of contemporary research to people who are not scientists. He has been science and medicine editor of *Newsweek*, science director of the Columbia Broadcasting System, a member of the editorial board of *Scientific American*, and president of the National Association of Science Writers. He is now working as a free-lance science writer and editor.

Mr. Pfeiffer's articles appear in numerous magazines, including the *New York Times Magazine*, *Coronet*, the *American Scholar*, *Harper's Bazaar*, and *America Illustrated*, and he has written about mental disease, brain research, radioactive fall-out and other subjects for network television shows such as "Conquest" and "Omnibus." He is consultant on public policy in science to the National Science Foundation, as well as to a number of industrial companies and universities. He is the author of *Science in Your Life*, *The Human Brain*, and, most recently, *The Changing Universe*, the story of radio astronomy, for which he received two Guggenheim fellowships.

Another award, this one a Fulbright fellowship, enabled

233

Mr. Pfeiffer to complete the writing of FROM GALAXIES TO MAN. In gathering material for this book he not only visited many American research centers, such as the Marine Biological Laboratory and the Mount Wilson and Palomar observatories, but spent six months abroad at laboratories in England, Switzerland, Denmark, Belgium, Germany and Italy. He also visited sites inhabited by early man, including prehistoric caves on the coast of the Mediterranean and elsewhere.

Mr. Pfeiffer travels with his wife, Naomi, who is an artist, and with his fourteen-year-old son Tony, who is interested in basketball and archeology, among other things. They live in New Hope, Pennsylvania.

234